DXing *on the* Edge

The Thrill of 160 Meters

By Jeff Briggs, K1ZM

Published by:
The American Radio Relay League, Inc.
Newington, CT 06111-1494

ABOUT THE COVER
Clockwise from upper left: JA7OEM's impressive and effective antenna system, Yamagata, Japan; K1ZM's Cape Cod QTH; "Mr 160," Stew Perry, W1BB; and the famous Point Shirley, Massachusetts, water tower from which he suspended his 160-meter antenna. The assortment of beautiful and exotic QSL cards show what's possible on Topband.

Contents

Foreword

We are very pleased to publish this book about the challenges and thrills of 160-meter DXing. The project started out as a sort of personal tribute by Jeff Briggs, K1ZM, to "Mr 160," Stew Perry, W1BB. While Jeff wrote this book to preserve and celebrate the early history of 160 meters, he has gone far beyond writing a simple historical narrative.

The title *DXing on the Edge—The Thrill of 160 Meters* says it all. It describes just how unpredictable—and yet exhilarating—Topband can be. While DXing can seem almost routine on 20 or 15 meters, there's no band like 160 meters to get your adrenaline pumping, especially when something really rare unexpectedly answers your CQ! And those exceedingly rare, delightful moments when 160-meter DX signals pound in at 599 *really do* make up for all the other times—when signals are 339 with deep QSB, while S9+10 dB static crashes challenge and frustrate the diehard Topbander. Making a Topband DX QSO is not for the fainthearted.

K1ZM chronicles 160-meter DXing from the early 1930s right through until today. He also describes in practical detail a variety of transmitting and receiving antennas that work for him as well as for other top-notch 160-meter DXers.

In fact, you can hear for yourself what some really long-haul, exotic DX contacts sound like on 160 meters. We have bundled with this book an audio CD, on which are preserved some really memorable QSOs made by prominent stations around the world.

I think you'll read this book and be inspired to do what I did: fire up my radio on 160 meters and check out the DX!

David Sumner, K1ZZ
Executive Vice President
Newington, Connecticut
October 1997

Dedication

This book is dedicated to Stewart S. Perry, W1BB, who led the way and demonstrated what was possible on 160 meters. It is also dedicated to those who follow in his footsteps today in search of the ultimate reward in DXing—the logging of another "new one" on 160 meters!

About the Author

Jeff Briggs, K1ZM, is a well-known 160-meter DXer and contester who developed a fascination with 160 meters in the late 1950s. Having read about the 160-meter accomplishments of W1BB in the pages of *QST*'s "How's DX?" column, written by Rod Newkirk, W9BRD, Jeff dreamed of the day when he too could join in on the fun on Topband. As a teenager with only a receiver and no transmitter, this would not become possible until nearly 20 years later.

While performing his military service from 1968 to 1972, Jeff used to listen to W1BB's enormous signal at sunrise in Bremerhaven, Germany. The receiving antenna there was a three-wire rhombic at 100 feet for 1.750 MHz. With such an antenna, signals from even the western USA were quite copiable in northern Germany.

Still lacking a transmitter at that time, Jeff corresponded often with W1BB, who was kind enough to send him periodic copies of his famous *160-Meter Newsletter*. This piqued Jeff's interest even more and at the 1973 New England ARRL Convention, he finally met Stew Perry in person. Stew was delivering a forum on the challenges of 160-meter DXing. A lengthy discussion ensued, some of which forms the basis for the early history of W1BB's career reported in this book. At the time, Stew Perry was 69 years old but still very active on Topband.

K1ZM's personal affection for Stew Perry and a genuine respect for his achievements on 160 meters formed the impetus for the creation of this work. It is altogether fitting and appropriate that the story of W1BB and of his peers in the early years of 160-meter DXing be preserved for others to read about and enjoy.

The author resides today in East Fishkill, New York, and on Cape Cod, Massachusetts. He is married with two children and can be found regularly on 160 meters pursuing his passion—chasing DX on Topband!

Acknowledgments

The author wishes to acknowledge the contributions of the following, without which this work would not have been possible:

Mike Tracy, KC1SX, Manager of the Technical Library at the American Radio Relay League Headquarters in Newington, Connecticut. Mike's assistance with the *QST* research necessary to recreate the chronology of W1BB's DXCC effort from 1930 to 1976 was invaluable.

Special thanks also are expressed to the ARRL in general and to K1ZZ, K1RO, N6BV, K5FUV and NC1L specifically, for their assistance and permission to incorporate W1BB's QSO data and the achievements of W1BB's contemporaries. These were extracted from *QST* and from DXCC Desk records.

Many others provided assistance with pictures, anecdotes, e-mails and personal remembrances of the period covered within the text. For this, the author is most grateful and wishes to recognize the following amateurs specifically: AA4V, AA0RS (G3SZA), DJ8WL, EA8AK, G3RBP, G3XTT, JA2GQO, JA5DQH, JE1CTM, K1MEM, K1PBW, K1VR, K2UVG, K2WI, K4PI, K9UWA, KG4W, KG7D, KI0G, N7CKD, N8PR, N0AX, NM7M, NO0Y, NW6N, ON4UN, PY1RO, VE1ZZ, VE3DO, VK6HD, W1BB, W1HT, W1JCC, W1JZ, W1UF, W2CRS/0, W4ZV, W8JI, W0UN, WB4ZNH, WB9Z, ZS5LB, ZS6EZ, 4S7RPG, 4X4NJ.

Special thanks are also expressed to K1PBW and to DJ8WL for their contributions to the audio CD portion of this work. Ernie's recording of Stew Perry, W1BB, made on December 31, 1977, serves as a memorable introduction to the audio CD. Peter's historical library of recordings at DJ8WL made possible many of the "memorable moments on 160 meters."

David Wilson, AA0RS (G3SZA), deserves special mention for allowing the use of his personal 160-meter photo collection, which made possible the inclusion of the photos of the early 160-meter "Olde Guarde" within the text. For all of these contributions, the author is most grateful.

About the
American Radio Relay League

The seed for Amateur Radio was planted in the 1890s, when Guglielmo Marconi began his experiments in wireless telegraphy. Soon he was joined by dozens, then hundreds, of others who were enthusiastic about sending and receiving messages through the air—some with a commercial interest, but others solely out of a love for this new communications medium. The United States government began licensing Amateur Radio operators in 1912.

By 1914, there were thousands of Amateur Radio operators— hams—in the United States. Hiram Percy Maxim, a leading Hartford, Connecticut, inventor and industrialist saw the need for an organization to band together this fledgling group of radio experimenters. In May 1914 he founded the American Radio Relay League (ARRL) to meet that need.

Today ARRL, with more than 170,000 members, is the largest organization of radio amateurs in the United States. The League is a not-for-profit organization that:

- promotes interest in Amateur Radio communications and experimentation
- represents US radio amateurs in legislative matters, and
- maintains fraternalism and a high standard of conduct among Amateur Radio operators.

At League headquarters in the Hartford suburb of Newington, the staff helps serve the needs of members. ARRL is also International Secretariat for the International Amateur Radio Union, which is made up of similar societies in more than 100 countries around the world.

ARRL publishes the monthly journal *QST*, as well as newsletters and many publications covering all aspects of Amateur Radio. Its headquarters station, W1AW, transmits bulletins of interest to radio amateurs and Morse code practice sessions. The League also coordinates an extensive field organization, which includes volunteers who provide technical information for radio amateurs and public-service activities. ARRL also represents US amateurs with the Federal Communications Commission and other government agencies in the US and abroad.

Membership in ARRL means much more than receiving *QST* each month. In addition to the services already described, ARRL offers membership services on a personal level, such as the ARRL Volunteer Examiner Coordinator Program and a QSL bureau.

Full ARRL membership (available only to licensed radio amateurs) gives you a voice in how the affairs of the organization are governed. League policy is set by a Board of Directors (one from each of 15 Divisions). Each year, half of the ARRL Board of Directors stands for election by the full members they represent. The day-to-day operation of ARRL HQ is managed by an Executive Vice President and a Chief Financial Officer.

No matter what aspect of Amateur Radio attracts you, ARRL membership is relevant and important. There would be no Amateur Radio as we know it today were it not for the ARRL. We would be happy to welcome you as a member! (An Amateur Radio license is not required for Associate Membership.) For more information about ARRL and answers to any questions you may have about Amateur Radio, write or call:

ARRL Educational Activities Dept
225 Main Street
Newington CT 06111-1494
(860) 594-0200
Prospective new amateurs call:
800-32-NEW HAM (800-326-3942)

Chapter 1

DXing on the Edge — The Thrill of 160 Meters!

DXing on 160 meters—or *Topband* as it is called by those who frequent it—presents complexities not encountered on the HF amateur bands. Even today, achievement of a 160-meter DXCC requires a combination of skill and perseverance matched perhaps only by a similar effort on 6 meters or moonbounce. 160-Meter DXCC holders have a justifiable sense of pride in their achievements. DXing on Topband is not for the faint-hearted.

This book reviews the history of DXing on 160 meters, from its inception in the 1930s to the present day at the end of the 1990s. It includes a number of personal anecdotes reported by those currently active on the band. It also provides the reader with some of the basic information necessary to join the fun.

We begin with a discussion of 160-meter propagation, a key factor influencing one's success as a DXer on the band.

160-METER PROPAGATION

Topband is unique when it comes to propagation, since signal absorption is higher on 1.8 MHz than on any other HF amateur band. Higher absorption levels mean weaker signals on 160 meters as signals travel from point A to point B. Stated another way, the amount of signal delivered between two points on 160 meters is nearly always less than on 80 meters due to the ability of electrons encountered along a path to absorb more signal energy on 1.8 MHz than on 3.5 MHz.

...communication between the antipodes on 160 meters on any path is far more difficult than on 80 meters.

In some respects, however, 160 meters does behave like 80 meters. Topband propagation peaks occur at local sunset on the western end of a path and again at local sunrise at the eastern terminus of a given path. However, unlike 3.5 MHz, 160 meters boasts far shorter openings in most directions and it suffers from deep QSB fading. This occurs over the course of minutes, as opposed to seconds on 80 meters, and is greatly impacted by the Earth's magnetic field.

The auroral ovals in the Earth's polar regions play a major role determining whether polar paths are possible on 160 meters and present severe obstacles to long-range communication, even in periods of moderate auroral disturbances. Given these facts, communication between the antipodes on 160 meters on any path is far more difficult than on 80 meters. Communication is nearly impossible to achieve on polar paths, except under exceptionally quiet circumstances, which may (or may not) occur during sunspot minima. On 160 meters, the operative DXing strategy is usually to "work it when you hear it!" On the most difficult paths, long-range openings may not occur again for years to come!

Atmospheric QRN also plays havoc on 160 meters, as it does on 80 meters. With generally weaker signal strengths available to work with on Topband, however, atmospheric QRN is a more compelling deterrent to long-range DX QSOs.

The challenge of DXing on 160 meters can be overcome, however, with kW power levels and effective transmitting and receiving antennas. Most successful Topband DXers will also quickly point out that lots of patience and perseverance are required if one is to achieve 160-Meter DXCC, along with a good set of well-trained ears.

Low-angle transmitting antennas usually work best on Topband, and most serious DXers also employ specialized receiving antennas to discrimininate against atmospheric noise. These include Beverages, receiving loops, receiving EWEs, low dipoles and the like. Even with the finest gear and antennas available, 160 meters often frustrates (read that as *humbles*) the very best operators in the world today. However, rather than take up some other simpler aspect of DXing (like another band perhaps), many say the challenges posed by Topband make it the most interesting band there is!

EARLY DXING ON 160 METERS

The post WW II DXCC program began accepting contacts for credit made after November 11, 1945, but this date by no means defines the beginnings of DXing on 160 meters. And while most of the early players have passed away and cannot tell us directly about it, enough documentation exists to give us a flavor of what it was like chasing DX on 1.8 MHz around 1930, when things began in earnest. And, yes, it *was* exciting and difficult beyond belief!

1930 is regarded by many as the inception of serious, organized DXing on 160 meters since it was in this year that the original "160 Meter Transatlantic DX Tests" sponsored by *Short Wave Magazine* began. In this era, you did not simply turn on your receiver and find the 160-meter band chock-full of S9 DX signals from one end of the band to the other. Rather, you might tune your homemade one-tube receiver for *days* before hearing a DX signal. And then, due to the low power levels and poor antennas involved, you might spend weeks or months before a successful contact might be made with a given target station.

...you might tune your homemade one-tube receiver for days before hearing a DX signal.

The "Transatlantic Tests" were intended to increase everyone's (and especially first-timers') chances of working DX and were held every Saturday morning during the prime winter season at European sunrise. The tests required close coordination of watches on both sides of the Atlantic. North American hams would call CQ for the first five minutes of each hour and then listen for the next five minutes when the Europeans would call. Occasionally a contact would actually be made and the calling schedule would be halted. From these humble beginnings, modern, organized DXing on 160 meters began.

These famous tests were organized by Peter Pennell, G2PL, and David Mitchell, G2II, and included a small group of others that first season. Most notable among these were Harry, G6GM; Ern, G3PU; Clarry Roach, VE1EA; and Stew Perry, W1BB. Others who excelled in their day and joined in shortly thereafter included W1DBM, G6UJ, W2UK, FA8BG, W3AJS, G6FO and G8BQ. However, one name in this very early group stands out— and that was Stew Perry, W1BB, who became the first to achieve DXCC on 160 meters some 46 years later. His achievements on 160 meters were unique and quite extraordinary for the time. They deserve special treatment in any serious discussion of 160-meter DXing in the postwar period.

Chapter 2

The Stew Perry Era (1930 to 1982)

Stewart S. Perry, a true pioneer in amateur radio, was born in 1904 and lived his entire life in a small Victorian house in Winthrop, Massachusetts, a suburb east of Boston. At the tender age of 8 years, he was inspired to become an amateur by listening to transmissions on a friend's crystal set. As Stew recalls it, he was playing one day in his backyard when his next-door neighbor, Eddy O'Toole, called him over for a demonstration of his crystal set.

Together they listened and Eddy explained that the dots and dashes they were hearing were coming from the Boston Navy

Fig 2-1—44 Pleasant Street, Winthrop, Massachusetts (at left in photo). Home QTH of W1BB. Stew maintained two 160-meter stations in this Victorian residence, where he lived his entire life.

Yard (station NAD). The operators were discussing the famous passenger liner Titanic that had just sunk. Accompanied by his friend Eddy, Stew then traveled to a local radio outlet in Boston called Bin's Radio to purchase parts for a crystal radio of his own. Not long thereafter, using a Quaker Oats cereal box and some wire for a coil, plus a galena crystal, Stew assembled his own radio and was himself copying NAD's transmissions.

Later that same year, Stew built his own spark transmitter using a Ford spark coil. He got on the air using a self-assigned callsign SS, his own first two initials. Even in those days, Stew had a big signal, since NAD used to call him from time to time to ask that he QRT because he was interfering with them! Stew recalls that his first QSO was with his neighbor Eddy O'Toole, followed by contacts with other friends around the neighborhood in Winthrop.

Some years later, when Stew was a teenager, the US government began issuing amateur operator licenses and Stew decided he should apply for one of his own. At that time, those holding real licenses would often "turn in" those operating illegally and Stew decided he better get a legitimate ticket.

Licensing tests in those days consisted of a code test at five words per minute. If you passed the code test, you were then allowed to take the written exam, which was a 100% essay affair covering electronic theory, rules and regulations. Applicants were also required to draw schematic diagrams of a station receiver, transmitter and antenna system. It so happened that Stew passed his exam on the very day that World War I began, so no station license was actually issued to him then.

Even in those days, Stew had a big signal...

When the war ended and station licenses again became available, Stew, then around 15 years old, decided to attempt to secure 1AA on the first day of issuance in 1919. Arising in the very wee hours, he traveled to Boston's Customs House, only to find a line ahead of him (about 27 to be exact). He was issued the callsign 1BB, instead of the desired 1AA, a callsign he would hold until his death in 1990.

In the post-WW I period, the 160-meter band covered frequencies from 1.750 to 2.000 MHz. Little in the way of DX was achieved initially, since signals from those early spark transmitters were figuratively as broad as a barn door! True single-signal selectivity did not occur until the development of the vacuum tube, following some of the early work of Dr. Lee DeForest.

DXing on 1.8 MHz in those days...one of the toughest challenges in ham radio.

Between about 1920 and 1926, Stew served as a commercial radio operator in the Merchant Marine, operating mainly in the 500-meter band. During this period he honed his CW skills and four years later, in 1930, he became an early organizer and participant in the aforementioned 160-Meter Transatlantic Tests.

In the early thirties, only a handful of countries along with the US and Canada allowed access to the band and most of the European stations active on 160 were restricted to only 10 W transmitter power. US stations in those early years also labored under severe power restrictions. (Following WW II and continuing right up through the 1970s, most US amateurs worked under *some* kind of nighttime power limitation on Topband. The ability for US amateurs to legally run meaningful power input levels on 160 meters did not occur until the shutdown of the US loran system about 1980.) These kinds of handicaps, coupled with the unique propagation characteristics cited earlier, made DXing on 1.8 MHz in those days one of the toughest challenges in Ham Radio.

Stew Perry's station in Winthrop could hardly be characterized as ordinary, however. He actually maintained a number of stations—two of them were located in his home in Winthrop and another one was located several miles away on the seacoast in Winthrop at a place called Point Shirley. There was also a summer home in Maine with a station and a mobile station for 160 meters in his car. He even had a station on his yacht, which he shared with his first wife Alice, W1DQF.

Let's begin with a description of Stew's primary station in his home. This was truly a vintage affair using home-brew equipment he built in the early 1930s. Single-band transmitters existed for each of the ham bands including 160, 80, 40, 20, 10, 5 and 2 meters. (There was nothing for 15 meters, since US amateurs did not receive access to 21 MHz until about 1952.) Through a home-brew patch cord system, band changes could be achieved in less than 10 seconds.

Stew also employed an all-band tuner, with plug-in coils and variable capacitors, to give him flexibility on all the bands. His primary transmit antenna on 160 meters from the home QTH was a 160-meter doublet, which was later replaced by an inverted L. The inverted L, by the way, became an antenna Stew did much to perfect as a transmitting antenna on Topband during his long DXing career. It continues to be the antenna of choice for many

*Point Shirley
is located on a
narrow spit of
land to the east
of downtown
Winthrop…*

new 160-meter DXers even today due to its simplicity and high degree of effectiveness. We will describe this antenna in complete detail in a later chapter in this book.

Stew's other station at his home was in his bedroom. He used this to follow late-night openings on 160 meters at European sunrise. If things really heated up on the band, you can almost imagine him drifting down to the main radio room, a cup of coffee in hand, to work the opening.

Stew's third station was the truly legendary one, which he developed out at Point Shirley several miles away. For those not familiar with the eastern suburbs around Boston, Point Shirley is located on a narrow spit of land to the east of downtown Winthrop, which itself sits on a peninsula jutting out into the Atlantic Ocean. Either location is in close proximity to salt water, but the Point Shirley site was a 160-meter DXers dream come true!

The station at Point Shirley was situated at a water tower. At

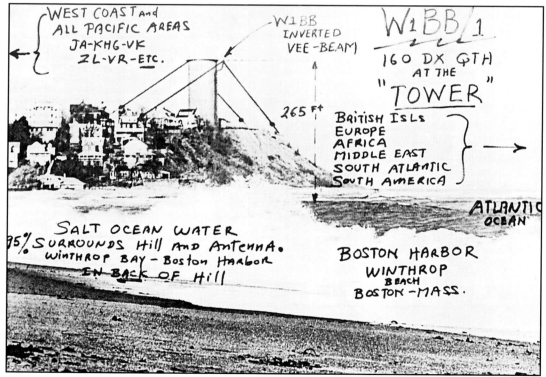

Fig 2-3—The famous W1BB/1 Point Shirley Site, as annotated by Stew Perry.

Fig 2-4—The water tower at Point Shirley as it looks today.

Fig 2-5—Looking toward Europe (60°) from the W1BB/1 water tower.

its base Stew maintained a station in a sort of bunkhouse with a cot for sleeping. Availability of this site was by special permission, granted as an outgrowth of Stew's participation in local Civil Defense activities. At this same location, operations were also conducted for the Winthrop Emergency Radio Net for which Stew served as radio officer. It was this special relationship combining public service with ham radio that allowed Stew to participate in some of the transatlantic tests from the water tower. Much later on, in the twilight of his amateur career, he also participated in 160-meter contests from there.

Stew's transmit antenna at Point Shirley was his remarkable V beam suspended from the top of the water tower. Viewed from the Atlantic Ocean offshore, the apex of the V was approximately 265 feet above the water level, with an unbelievable takeoff over saltwater in nearly all directions. The principal exception was due west, back across Boston harbor. A variety of listening antennas down on the beach below completed the station setup. It should be noted that the location was free of most man-made noise. Stew had problems, from time to time, with kids vandalizing his receiving antennas but it was a small price to pay when one considers the unbelievable capability of the station.

In the first years of the Transatlantic tests, Stew and his peers did not think much of the adventure as one of counting countries for DXCC, as we might think of it today. The thrill of just making a contact with a European station was enough motivation for him and the early players. Stew did begin counting countries in 1935 when he worked and received a QSL from ON4AU in Belgium as his country #1. It is odd that Belgium should turn out to be Stew's first DXCC country, considering that for many years after WW II, Belgian hams were denied access to Topband. They only regained it on January 1, 1987.

Some years later, others followed Stew's lead and began counting their 160-meter countries as well, including Charlie O'Brien, W2EQS, and Larry Connell, W1LYV. Gradually, as more countries came on the band, new pioneers in their respective countries began appearing, including Paddy, EI9J; Mick, ZL3RB; Armin, DL1FF; Jan, DL9KR, and John, VK5KO. New faces emerging in the US and taking a big interest in the band included Willie, W8GDQ; Sam, W2IU; Alex, W9NH (W6KIP); Roy, W1TX; John, WØGDH (W5SUS); Gordy, VE2UQ (VE5XU);

Fig 2-6—John Dormois, W0GDH (now W5SUS) of Kansas City. John was one of the well-known early players from the Midwest.

Ralph, W1HGT (W1HT); Roy, WA7DOL/6; Herb, W0VXO (KV4FZ); Bob, W0GTA (EP2BK, VS1LP, 9M4LP) and Earl, W5RTQ (K6SE).

Still later, others joining the fray included Wal, WB8APH (W8LRL); Ernie, K1PBW; Jim, W2DEO; Gene, W4BRB; Arlan, N4OO; Willem, PA0HIP; Mike, GD4BEG; Rolf, PY1RO; Dave, G3SZA (AA0RS); Isaji, JA3AA; Tom, WA8IJI (W8JI) and Cliff, W1PPN. We will profile some of these stations in more detail in a later chapter.

Among Stew Perry's many 160-meter contributions was one that was enormously popular among his fellow 160-meter DXers for 50 years. This was the production and distribution of his famous *W1BB 160-Meter DX Bulletin*, which he and his wife assembled by hand on a typewriter at home. This chronicled the goings-on and achievements of those on Topband. For half a century Stew would collect various tidbits from those active on 160 meters and then assemble them into one of the finest Topband publications ever made available. Sometimes a copy will turn up at a major hamfest but the originals are quickly becoming collector's items!

Stewart S. Perry
36 Pleasant Street
Winthrop, Massachusetts

Al..DX/join on

THANKYOU for the QSP from VE8MOA by your QSO with
him at HE1AB - very glad to get confirmation of his dates

CONGRATULATIONS to you for such a VFB "Advent" into 160m DX
chalking up already 58C in your first full season GREAT!!! Keep up
the good work!! (Sorry the PA1AE didnt go thru though!!

HEREWITH copy of latest 160m DX Bulletin - hope that you
find something of interest herein!!

HAPPY SUMMER and then b.c.n.u. for 81/82 160m DXing season

73 de Stew/W1BB

MAY 1, 1981   W1BB --- 160 METER DX BULLETIN --- W1BB   1980/1981 - No.2
                                        Since 1932
de W1BB/Stew --- 160 is a Suprising and wonderful DX Band!! Condx being generally quite poor, with
an unusual amount of absorbtion, short skip or none, and Oodles on QRN - many of us thot, maybe
"This Is It" - NO real '80/'81 DX!! However, spotty though it was all season, it sure uncorked some
wonderful suprises. Quite a few say "one of the best Yrs I've had!!" We've ALL griped abt the poor
& erratic Cndx. ACTUALLY though, arent they part of the fun and challenge?? The more difficult, the
more thrill/satisfaction of accomplishment! We learn the lesson WELL, that if you arent "Johnny on
the SPOT" to get in on the excellent and unexpected openings that do pop-up, it seldom if ever
happens again - you've missed it, goodbye/DX! BUT if you're there - WOW!! what fun!! --- Like K2GNC,
Bill, right on the button, Peak/wise & wkd 3 JAs in a row for "FIRST EVER" JA/W-NE Coast (W1,2,3,)
plus VKs 3,4,5,6, in a row!!!! Made possible by the MOMENTOUS event (we have ALL been waiting for),
cessation of LORAN on 1900Kcs, and the JAs(1907½-1912½Kcs)were coming thru!! W2EQS/9-Chas immediatel
had JA2GQO,9EB,30NB,5DQH & Otrs skipping into W4EX and KA7BTQ/lands especiallyMuch fun and excitemen
(.. Sunrise times!! Hopefully one of these days W1 will QSO JA??? Maybe W1BB (Hope-Hope!!), that IS,
IF we can get over/under or around that AURORAL OVAL on this path!! THEN VS6DO/Paul on 1835 made son
some real excitement/fun, working W8LRL and Otrs Hr and in EU especially & Asia!! Also wkd AA1K/"Jo
CHEERS!! An achievement!! ---- VE1ZZ/Jack Unexpectedly QSO'd VK6HD/Mich Long-Path, 2130z,449x2,1802kc
Jan25. Most UNUSUAL!! (Also VE1BVL!) ----(VK6HD's signal always vy "Potent" this yr!!) ---- ALSO!!!
two resounding "FIRST-EVERS" :: W7RM/Rush wkd UK2RDX Jan25 0600z!!! & LA5HE/Rag wkd W7FS/Keith, FEB
14 0525z(Keith thinks,directly over POLE! ---- USSR Stations coming on 160, opened up possibilities
for 18 additional Countries!! and MANY were worked all over the world including W/VE!! (1850-55Kcs)
NEW Countries on,EA8,EA/Spain,OZ1LO made it possible for W1BB to Total 156 DXCC Countries Wkd/160m.
EL2FY/LIBERIA coming on unexpectedly gave many a "NEW-ONE"!!--G3PQA/5W8-John came on Jan31, gave out
many "New Ones", Mostly EUs, but sum Ws & QRT Mar31!! ------- EL2AV also on!! ---- To name some of
the "Highlights"!! So Gess cant say'80/81 TOOOooooo.... bad - can we??!! Additionally CQ/CW Test
pulled their annual "Rabbit out of the Hat" for a corking good 2nd night!! But yes, except for the
"Highlights" the BANDwas way down in many respects!! Those who say it was a POOR season, and those
who say it was a GOOD season are BOTH right, depending on how lucky they were!! GREAT game tho- eh??
These UNUSUAL results, and others, highlight the News, making '80/'81 a unique season,(In fact there
are so many 160m Items, afraid we'll run out of space and not get them all in!!! That'll be a pity!!
And Apologies to you good fellows who sent, for "Tid-Bits" you sent, we cant use,for lack of space!! Sorry
K1PBW/Ernie sez:"I do miss what the band was in the 1960s. I think that was the GOLDEN AGE of 160 -
believe you'll agree - unfortunately few of the same fellows are on now & not many have come to take
their places - sort of the "End of an Era"!! (Yes, sort of true Ernie - know what you mean - yet
there are a few outstanding pioneering type DXers still on 160, unusual Dx being wkd, and the
CHALLENGE of TOP BAND, still there for those who want it!!) Altho YOU left very few Challenges unMET
W1BB/Stew Sez:Found it necessary to "Slack Off" a bit on DXing, as previously indicated.'Taint much
fun, not to be able to stay up on 160 all night, or into the "Wee small hours", to snag the EXOTIC,
& be in on ALL the Fun!! No 'dyed in the wool' DXer, likes to "Miss-One". However, "Father Time
Keeps Marching On", and we have to take cognizance, whether we like it or not, but "Philosophically"
and in good spirit! - N'est-ce Pas? Did fairly well tho, and thoroughly enjoyed every minute!
Will continue in the same mood, being thankful for the VFB pleasures and THRILLS on 160m!!!
       HAPPY SUMMER!!   B.C.N.U. Come FALL and '81/82 Season   73! de Stew'n Marguerite

Fig 2-7—Part of one of W1BB's famous 160-Meter Bulletins.

These bulletins described notable band openings, stories of interesting contacts, antenna design discussions, the tracking of DXCC milestones, expedition news, the Transatlantic Test announcements and subsequent results, new regulatory happenings on 160 meters and hundreds of other genuinely interesting topics.

The best part was that the price to receive one was *free*! All one needed to do was send in a piece of 160-meter news to Stew or accomplish something notable on the band and you were sent a copy, even if you did not ask for one. Stew, it seemed, kept track of everyone and every achievement that occurred on Topband each season. And then he was kind enough to share it with others to maintain interest in the band.

This last point was a significant one and today's followers of 160 meters owe W1BB a major debt of gratitude for demonstrating what was possible on Topband. At various points during his long career on 160 meters, there were discussions regarding taking 1.8 MHz away from US and world amateurs. The world frequency allocation conferences were always uncertain times for 160-meter devotees, not to mention WW II, when the band was lost to the US for over seven years. But, through Stew's vigilance and a Herculean effort on the part of the ARRL after WW II, Topband was preserved for others to enjoy today. It is remarkable indeed how much current lovers of 160 meters owe this one man. Were it not for his efforts in the early years, which were then buttressed by the contemporaries he inspired along the away, 160 meters might not be an amateur band today.

Apart from the obvious operating achievements, the measure of any man is what *others* say about him. From all accounts of the man, written and verbal, it is clear Stew Perry was genuinely admired and respected by those who knew him. Time and time again the word *gentleman* comes up in references to him. So too do stories of his special gift of helping others acquire skills on the band. It is said that he *never* gave up on a weak station calling him, knowing perhaps that the caller might need him for a "new one." In later years, his 160-Meter Tests essentially became "first timers' nights" where newer DXers might chase needed countries from an enlarged pool of listeners looking out for them on the other side of the pond.

Ernie, K1PBW, one of Stew's contemporaries on the band

> *The best part was that the price to receive one was* **free***!*

Fig 2-8—Stew Perry, W1BB, in his shack at 44 Pleasant Street, Winthrop, Massachusetts.

Fig 2-9—W1BB with Aki, JA5DQH, at the water tower QTH: 160-Meter DXCC #1 and Asian 160-Meter DXCC #1 together!

and someone who knew him well, had the following comments: "As I recall, Stew's efforts in keeping Topband open to amateur radio after WW II accounts for why we had a band in use, loran being such a mighty power to contend with after the war. Stew did not want to see the band gobbled up by commercial or government interests, either here or abroad, and for many years, his newsletter was the only organized voice for amateur radio operation on 160. Stew Perry devoted much of his life to the community of operation on 160 meters. He was a wonderful person, full of the natural, old-time goodness and cheer that often came with those who were born in the early 1900's. He was a father, if not a grandfather, to the community of activity that grew up on Topband after the war, having been one of its pioneers before the war when Amateur Radio was in its infancy."

When he was not working DX on 160 meters, Stew was usually contributing in other ways. He wrote often about DXing on Topband and was a frequent speaker at DX forums, conventions and hamfests. Scores of stations refer to him as their "160-meter Elmer," including such well-known Topband DXers as 4X4NJ, ZS5LB, K1ZM and G3SZA. It is said that the naming of 160 meters as "the Gentleman's Band" was, in part, a reference to the kind of operating style and courtesy displayed by W1BB as he approached DXing on 1.8 MHz.

In 1968, 33 years after starting to count countries on 160 meters, Stew worked and confirmed his 100th country on 1.8 MHz, CE3CZ. Formal certification as 160-Meter DXCC #1, however, would not occur until November 1, 1976, the date on which the ARRL first made single-band 160-Meter DXCCs available. Illness in his later years prevented Stew from ever filing for 160-meter endorsements once they became available. It is known that he reached at least the 156 level, and perhaps one or two countries more. His exact mix of countries worked was never kept on file at the ARRL DXCC Desk, as early non-endorsable 160-Meter DXCCs did not require the keeping of such records. You merely had to present valid confirmations from 100 countries. These were verified, returned to the applicant and an award was issued. The original 160-Meter DXCC awards were never intended to be endorsable. Endorsable 160-Meter DXCCs came some years later when, in response to a high level of interest, the current 160-Meter DXCC program was introduced.

...he reached at least the 156 level, and perhaps one or two countries more.

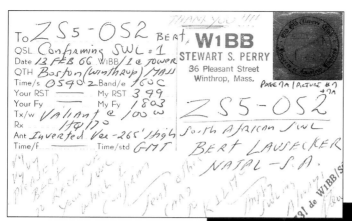

Fig 2-10—One of W1BB's well known 160-meter QSLs. This one was sent to ZS5LB in 1966 to acknowledge Bert's SWL report of W1BB's signal in South Africa, at RST 349. At the time Bert had SWL call ZS5-052. Later, he was licensed as ZS5LB and achieved African DXCC #1. Bert notes that W1BB's influence was a major factor in his becoming interested in Topband.

In spite of the lack of official records, much of Stew's story is known through articles in *QST* and other publications, and thankfully is not lost forever. Many outstanding QSOs are known to have been made, including ones with VS1LP (9V1), EP2BK, VP8GQ and 4W1AE (G3PQA). While he was heard many times in Japan, he never did complete a contact with JA. This was due to interference in the USA caused by the loran navigational system. Just about the time that loran operations shut down (1980) and US power levels were increased to a kW in most places, Stew was forced to begin curtailing his 160-meter activities. He was heard infrequently on the band in the early 1980s. He spent the last years of his life in a nursing home and passed away in 1990.

The complete story of Stew Perry's 160-meter activities could easily fill volumes. I shall present a timeline of his milestones, in summary form, along with some of the notable achievements of his peers. There will also be highlights of each period, where appropriate. In this way, Stew's progress toward 160-Meter DXCC can almost be recreated, interwoven with some of the firsts achieved by his contemporaries. Taken together, it is an exciting story indeed!

Much of the material that follows has been taken from *QST*, the official journal of the American Radio Relay League in Newington, CT, and is used with permission. The author wishes to express his sincere thanks to the ARRL for its invaluable contribution to this section. We will begin with 1930, as this was the first year in which the 160-Meter Transatlantic Tests were conducted.

Chapter 3

160-Meter DXing Chronology, 1930 to 1949

At this time, 160 meters is largely an AM phone band. US amateurs report that only 1.5% of their activity is on 160-meter CW. The US band is 1.750 to 2.000 MHz. UK amateurs request receiving reports of their signals on 1.715 MHz. W6 is hearing W9 on AM phone. Maryland is hearing W5 and W9 on AM phone. Iowa is hearing W2 and W3 on AM phone.

UK hams conduct tests on 1.750 MHz to prove the present-day utility of the band. Transmit stations are limited to 1 W for tests. Winners of early tests include G6YL, G6ZH and EI7C.

IARU takes over administration of WAC awards from ARRL. From 1926 to 1930 only 566 WAC awards have been issued; by November 1935, only 21 phone WACs have been issued.

There is only a handful of countries available on Topband and not all allocations overlap. SM amateurs conduct 1.75 MHz tests using crystal control. The ionosphere is referred to as "Father Heaviside."

W1BB makes his first QSOs to Europe, mainly into the UK. On November 11, 1934, W4CPG is heard Q4/S5 in *Japan* on 160-meter AM phone and receives the SWL card to prove it! In December 1934, W1DIK in Rumford, RI, is heard on 1.75 MHz by G5BI and BRS 1422. In February 1935, W1HUJ in Cromwell, Connecticut, is heard by G5BI.

On February 10, 1935, Phil Rand, W1DBM, in Connecticut works G2II with S6-9 signals and is heard also by G5WU and

BRS 1089. UK stations are now running 10 W on 1.75 MHz. On February 14, 1935, W5DVK makes two historic QSOs on AM phone with Hawaii (then K6) and YWC, an experimental station in Venezuela. The 1935 ARRL DX Test, conducted from March 9 to March 17, 1935, is memorable. W6AHI works K6CRU in Hawaii. On March 10, 1935, G2II works VE1EA for the first ever G/VE QSO on Topband. On March 9, 1935, at 0547Z W1BB, running 500 W input power, works ON4AU and at 0620Z works G5BY. W8HMJ hears G5AB calling W1BB. W1BB's signal is heard for 35 minutes *after* UK sunrise! It is noted for the first time that USA signals peak up for a brief period at sunrise on the eastern end of the path in the UK.

B. Wickham, G2DW, copies W1HYK, W2DFB and W2HI on AM phone. On CW he copies W2GCE, W2GJC and W8ASI. G5WP/EA8 SWLing in Tenerife using a one-tube receiver copies over 80 USA stations as far West as W6! He hears W3UZ and W8CHL on AM phone. Most USA signals are S3-4 in EA8.

D. S. Mitchell, G2II, in north Wales from February 2 to March 1, 1935, copies 15 stations as far West as W8, including VE1EA, W1BB, W3AJS and W8ASI. SWL BRSFM copies W8GBD and W9ABQ. On April 1, 1935, the Canadian band is reset to 1.775 MHz to 2.000 MHz (losing 1.715 to 1.775 MHz). A suggestion is made to reschedule the 160-Meter Transatlantic Tests to the period from mid-January to mid-March to increase the possibility of more QSOs.

As these events are taking place, the very first 10-meter WACs ever are recorded. W3FAR gets #1 on October 12, 1935, running 22 W. ZS1H is #2 on October 13, 1935, followed by W7AMX on October 23, 1935. The RST system is revised to a 9 level system of reporting, our current standard, as of October 1935.

160-METER DXING CHRONOLOGY, 1936 TO 1939

1936

The 1936 160-Meter Tests are conducted from 05-07Z on Friday/Saturday nights from January 24 to March 15, 1936. On February 23, 1936, W1BB makes the first-ever QSO between North America and Africa, working FA8BG in Algeria about

0500Z. "Tommy" Thomas, W2UK, also makes a QSO shortly thereafter.

1936 ARRL DX Test has W1BB making two transatlantic QSOs with Europe. W1BB also makes 32 QSOs with G stations during the Winter 1936 season, plus a QSO with EA4AO in Spain.

The 1936 season on 160 meters suffers as the solar cycle is nearing the sunspot maxima that year. On the old 5-meter band (56 MHz), some unbelievable SWL reports are made. On April 10 and November 1, 1936, Wales copies W2JCY on 56-MHz AM phone. On September 12, 1936, W2IIQ is also copied in Wales. On January 10, 1937, G5BY is copied by W2HXD.

Regrettably, no QSOs are made in this period and these are among what is to become only a *handful* of transatlantic propagation reports ever recorded on the old 5-meter band. Before this band is changed to its present range from 50 to 54 MHz, the best-ever reported QSO on 5 meters is from the East Coast to the West Coast at a distance of approximately 2400 miles. It was made on July 22, 1938, between W1EYM and W6DNS on AM phone.

In April 1936 Charlie O'Brien, W2EQS, of Jersey City, New Jersey, issues a challenge to see who will achieve the first WAS award on 160 meters. The boys were not yet ready to contemplate the possibility of a 160-Meter WAC or DXCC.

Other notable events in 1936 were:

1) *QST*'s Operating News section now sports a new sub-section for the first time in the December issue. It's called "How's DX?". (2) FCC raises the US code-speed requirement from 5 to 13 wpm. (3) W2IOP arrives on the scene; famed 10-meter DXer J2HJ dies at the age of 26.

1937

A significant first on Topband is reported in 1937 as W9ROQ (Illinois) makes a QSO on 160-meter AM phone with W6IGA/K6 on Jarvis Island. The first Transatlantic Tests in 1937 report that on January 10, 1937, at 0212Z, W1BMW is copied by G2TM on 1.755 MHz with an RST of 339.

On March 6, 1937, W1BB QSOs G2DQ and on March 13, 1937, G2DQ and G2PL. David Brown, ZL1HY, well known to 160-meter DXers, is profiled in *QST* during 1937. G2II is now heard on 160 meters under his new call G6AA. The UK creates

The 1936 season on 160 meters suffers as the solar cycle is nearing the sunspot maxima that year.

separate call sign blocks for Scotland (GM) and for Wales (GW). VKs have 160 meters by special permission; maximum power input is limited to 25 W. It is noted that the following countries do *not* yet have access to 160 meters under the Madrid accords: OE, OH, PA, DL, LA, and CT. HB9 stations *do* have 160 meters by special permit.

Prewar DXCC is announced September 1937. W8CRA achieves prewar DXCC #1 in November 1937 with 112 confirmed.

1938

In the Second Annual 160-Meter WAS Party conducted on February 17, 1938, Gus Browning, W4BPD, (later destined to become one of the finest HF DXpeditioners of the 1960s), manages to work 37 states. W9UWL also snags 37. An interesting article by W6GPY appears in April 1938 *QST*. It describes a tuned-loop receiving antenna for the 160-meter ARRL HQ station, W1MK, which becomes W1AW to honor Hiram Percy Maxim, founder of the ARRL.

QST notes that for the princely sum of $3 US, amateurs can enjoy ARRL membership, a *QST* subscription and receive a copy of *The ARRL Handbook* too. (This sounds like the deal of the century!) December 1938 *QST* reports that G2PL and W1BB are active on the band. VS3RD is looking for QSOs as well. Year-end 1938 DXCC totals show several stations at or nearing the 140 country mark.

1939

W4EPP is reported by W1BB to have achieved an almost unbelievable QSO (for the period) with KC4USB on 160-meter AM phone. How remarkable to be able to communicate with Antarctica at all on 160 meters—let alone on AM phone!

160-METER DXING CHRONOLOGY, 1940 TO 1949

1940

In the 1940 160-Meter WAS Party, W9JYW, operating from Nebraska City, NE, manages to work 41 states using 300 W into a

$^1/_4$-wave inverted-L antenna with radials. His receiver is a Hammarlund HQ-120, one of the finer receivers available at the time.

After the outbreak of WWII in Europe, USA amateurs are precluded from communicating with the combatant countries. While the prewar DXCC program had continued, albeit in a somewhat reduced form, the program is finally suspended in December 1940. Final prewar DXCC totals of the leaders are announced in December 1940 *QST* as: W2GT 152, W6GRL 151, W8CRA (DXCC #1) 149, W2GTZ 148, W2GW 146, G6WY (DXCC #5) 145.

While it is not known with certainty, W1BB *probably* closed out his prewar DXCC effort with *fewer* than 10 countries worked on the 160-meter band. QSOs are known to have been made with W, VE, G, EA, ON, and FA8, as these were noted specifically in the reporting journals of the period. Most likely, W1BB also worked 3 WAC continents, including North America, Europe and Africa. Perhaps only one QSO with South America occurred on Topband prior to WW II, that being the W5DVK QSO with experimental station YWC. Only several stations are known to have worked Oceania prior to WW II. These were from the W5 and W6 call sign districts. While it may have been possible for W5DVK to have worked Europe for his fourth continent on Topband, it was not reported.

Thus, it appears that W1BB most likely led 160-Meter DXCC participants when the FCC shut down the band, with fewer than 10 countries worked. He was tied most likely for WAC on the band, with 3 continents worked.

1941 TO 1945, THE WAR YEARS

This is a dark period for all US amateurs. ARRL continues to publish *QST* but advertisements describe receivers and emphasize commitment to the war effort. National, Hallicrafters, Collins, Hammarlund, RME and the others of the day display distinctly muted advertisements in *QST*.

When the war ends, emphasis clearly shifts to the promotion of new technologies developed during the war for the US military. Eimac makes a big splash in *QST* with their transmitting-tube line and cleverly uses advertisements profiling ARRL DX Contest winners who have achieved top scores using their tubes.

Of the meaningful DX bands, only 10 meters is returned to US hams on November 15, 1945. The FCC announces in July 1945 its intention *not* to return 160 meters to amateurs due to development of the loran navigational system during WW II. The ARRL, to its credit, embarks on a Herculean effort to attempt a reconciliation with the FCC on this issue.

1946

Part of 80 meters is restored on March 31, 1946. A new band, 11 meters, becomes available at 27 MHz on March 15, 1946, complementing 10 meters as the premier DX band of the period. On May 9, 1946, the balance of 80 meters is restored. In July 1946 *QST* the ARRL argues strongly for a *shared* use of 160 meters with the loran system and an exclusive segment at 1.750 to 1.800 MHz for amateur use. Many letters to *QST*, however, indicate an attitude of "Who cares?" It seems as if the battle to resurrect 160 meters will be lost.

On July 1, 1946, part of 40 meters is restored. On November 2, 1946, all of 40 and 20 meters have been restored, but 40 meters is CW only. The US phone brethren are very unhappy about the lack of phone privileges on 7 MHz.

1947

The postwar DXCC program is in full-swing. The ARRL DXCC desk is attempting to reconcile the prewar and postwar DXCC countries lists. Charlie Mellen, W1FH, achieves the honor of postwar DXCC #1.

At the Atlantic City international conference held in May 1947, the ARRL proposes shared use of 1.8 to 2.0 MHz by amateurs and loran, on a non-interference basis. The FCC indicates it will study the merits of the proposal. This is the first crack in the wall on the subject.

Meanwhile, the solar cycle has reached another maximum, and on the new 6-meter VHF band, now 50 to 54 MHz, a new world record is reported on January 25, 1947, between KH6DD and J9AAK in Japan at 4600 miles! It is also noted that USA TV channel #1 at 50 to 54 MHz has been deleted

In a startling and unexpected move, the FCC restores 160 meters to US amateurs in March 1949.

on June 14, 1946. On April 10, 1947, 11 meters is shifted downward to cover 27.160 to 27.430 MHz. The upper 50 kHz of 20-meter phone is lost in October 1947, with the band now stopping at 14.350 MHz.

1948

There is little progress on the return of 160 meters to the amateur fraternity. The FCC continues to study the matter and also tests possible interference to loran by amateurs at low power levels.

1949

In a startling and *unexpected* move, the FCC restores 160 meters to US amateurs in March 1949. Amateurs get back an allocation from 1.8 to 2.0 MHz with many restrictions, especially in parts of Region 2 and Region 3. Still, for most of the lower 48 states, power levels are set generally at 500 W input power during the day and 200 W during the night.

In the May 1949 issue of *QST* an interesting how-to article appears on developing 160-meter DX antennas. The ARRL is obviously encouraging a rapid repopulation of the band to secure its future use. In June 1949 *QST*, a small blurb mentions that amateurs on 160 meters are now feverishly chasing 160-meter WAC. Who will be the first to achieve all continents on Topband?

On December 15, 1949, W4NNN/Ø (WØNWX) works G3PU on 1.810 MHz with 190 W for what is one of the first postwar 160-meter transatlantic QSOs. W1BB and W1EFN make it across to G and VE1EA makes a QSO with GD3UB on December 19, 1949. W9BRD, editor of *QST*'s "How's DX?" column, notes in the February 1950 issue of *QST* that, while this QSO is quite remarkable, the concept of a postwar WAC on 160 meters still seems pretty far fetched. Folks were still not considering the prospect of a 160-Meter DXCC yet either.

Chapter 4

160-Meter DXing Chronology, 1950 to 1959

1950

W1BB, VE1EA and others report working many Gs, GD3UB, GM8UM and FA8BG. W1BB is reported as S9+ at G2PL. In February 1950 EK1AO in Tangier is heard on the band. Other active stations include GW8WJ, DL2DV, EI3ET, many OKs, HZ1KE, PY7WS and KV4AA.

1951

On January 7, 1951, W1BB works EK1AO and follows this up on January 21, 1951, with a QSO with HC1JW. This is a new continent for WAC for Stew, his fourth. VE1EA also scores bigtime in January with a QSO to HZ1KE, the first-ever North America-to-Asia contact made on 160 meters. This is Clarry's fourth continent on Topband. W8HSW and W9PNE, in the heartland, also report QSOs with EK1AO. W9PNE's QSO was his first 160-meter DX QSO since 1941 and was made with 130 W. His receiver was a "three tube blooper."

W9CVQ is rewarded with QSOs with GW3ZV and GW3FSP. W2EQS works many Gs, GW3ZV and EK1AO. W2QHH, running less than 25 W, also makes the grade to GW3ZV. In a truly stunning late-season report, ZL1AH and ZL1MP report hearing W9CVQ's signals in Tauranga, New Zealand from 0642-0700Z at RST 329.

VE1EA now reports 10 countries worked on 160 meters, needing only Oceania and South America for WAC. W1LYV reports an AM phone QSO with GW3ZV, CW QSOs with dozens of Gs, plus GD3UB and EK1AO. ZL1AH reports hearing both W9CVQ and W1BB in mid-October. W4NNN/Ø (later WØNWX, ARRL president and now VP2VI), reports skeds with ZL1BY.

1952

...East-Coast loran stations are now running megawatt power on 160 meters...

This is a slow season on 160 meters. W2EQS reports that East-Coast loran stations are now running megawatt power on 160 meters, making DX reception difficult indeed. OH3NY and ZC4XP report hearing W1BB on their side. In other happenings of the time, the US gets a new band at 21 MHz called 15 meters. US Novices also gain a segment of the new band.

The 1952 to 1953 160-Meter Transatlantic Tests are announced by W1BB. These are to be held in January/February 1953 with W/VE amateurs transmitting on the hour for 5 minutes and DX stations transmitting for 5 minutes thereafter. On December 28, 1952, Bob Denniston, WØNWX, bags ZL1NX, who transmits around 1.903 MHz. In a letter to W2EQS, ZL1NX (ex-G6YS) explains that he used 5 W to a long wire at 80 feet to make the QSO. He notes this was his first QSO ever outside ZL.

1953

A year of many highlights! W1BB works OH3NY for a new one. W2EQS snags VP4LZ for his first South American. Charlie now has 12 countries on Topband, having made two-ways with GI2ARS and KP4KD. He uses a Viking I, an HRO receiver and a 275-foot long-wire antenna, only 25 feet high.

In the heartland, W5ENE manages to corral several Gs on January 4, 1953. W9PNE now has eight countries and three continents on Topband towards his WAC, using 160 W, a 14-MHz V and a BC-224 receiver. W3EIS (later well-known as W3IN/N4IN) makes the grade as well, connecting with several Gs and KP4DV. Don's signals are also reported as being heard by ZS3K, ZL1AH and OH3NY. Gene Sykes, W4BRB, of 80-meter fame, discovers 160 meters to his liking and is now often on the band. Gene will later become one of the early DXCC holders on Topband, securing #6 on February 14, 1977.

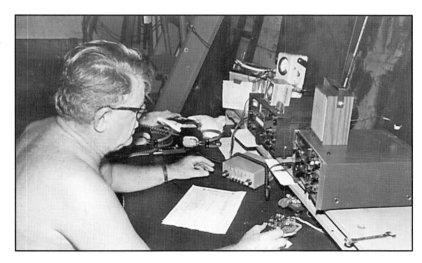

Fig 4-1—Gene Sykes, W4BRB (now W4OO), holder of 160-Meter DXCC #6.

On March 8, W1BB scores with the first-ever USA-Asia QSO on Topband, when he works ZC4XP, who used a balloon-supported vertical for an antenna. This is Stew's fifth continent on 160 meters—only Oceania is lacking for WAC #1 on Topband. VE1EA worked ZC4XP a week earlier for his second Asian QSO. Clarry now has 12 postwar DXCC counters on 160 meters and four continents (14 DXCC countries overall, counting his prewar efforts).

W1BB is consistently heard by ZS3K in SW Africa, but no two-way QSO has yet occurred. Stew is also heard by ZL1AH on March 1, 1953, but no QSO is achieved. Just as the summer static sets in, W2WWP breaks through with an East-Coast QSO to ZL1WW on 1899/1904 kHz at 1030Z on May 3, 1953. W2WWP manages to repeat the QSO two times on skeds before the band folds for the summer.

Ever-changing frequency allocations now find Gs mainly between 1825 to 1875 kHz, ZLs at 1975 to 1900 kHz and Ws in three zones: 1800 to 1825 kHz, 1875 to 1900 kHz and from 1975 to 2000 kHz.

As summer turns into fall, ZL1AH breaks through to G6GM three times in mid-October in what are the first-reported 12,000 mile antipodal QSOs ever made on 160 meters. 4X4s are trying to get permission to join in on the fun, but so far no luck. In the heartland, W9NH scores with LU4DM on 1.907 MHz. Stations reported gearing up on the band include GC3, HA, HB9, YO and 3A2.

W1BB closes out the year in fine style, snagging ZL1WW in late 1953 to achieve the first-ever WAC on Topband! In other news, the FCC decides to grant a phone subband on 40 meters, much to the delight of the 7-MHz crowd.

1954

Another year of spectacular doings on 160 meters. VR2BJ (Fiji) on 1.885 MHz scores with first-ever QSOs with WØAPF, WØFIM, WØIFH and W3RGQ at East-Coast sunrise. W9PNE and many others snag CN2AO in Tangier. This is followed by a QSO with HC1KV. This brings W9PNE's numbers up to 12 countries/ 4 continents. Neighbor W9NH now sports 14 and 5 respectively. Joe, K2ANR, puts in a big showing on 160 meters and works into Europe, Africa and New Zealand.

WØNWX now sports two 1100-foot long-wires and is up to 18 countries and five continents on 160 meters. Vic Clark, W4KFC, often frequents the band and is reported to have a huge

Fig 4-2—Bob Eshleman, W4QCW (now W4DR, right) with Dave Schmocker, KJ9I (left). Bob holds 5BDXCC award #1 and has over 275 confirmed on Topband.

signal in Europe. Sadly, OH3NY reports the loss of 1.8 MHz in Finland, although he still listens in from time to time. In a major coup, W9FIM using a 93-foot vertical and 150 W, works ZL3RB on AM phone.

There is some *real* DX active on Topband now, including CN2, EL, GC, GD, GI, GM, GW, HB, HC, HK, KH6, KP4, KV4, KZ5, LU, TI, VP4, VP9, VP7, VQ4, VR2, VR3, VS1, YI, YU1, YV5, ZB1, ZC4, ZC5, ZS3 and ZL. In total, there are over 30 countries on all six continents known to be active on 160 meters in the early 1954 season!

The legendary Katashi Nose, KH6IJ, begins appearing late season on the band and scores with W2QHH, W9PNE and many others. KH6MG is also active and works W1BB and W3RGQ. In October 1954, a teenage Bob Eshleman, W4QCW, and others activate Navassa Island, as KC4AB. Bob is known as W4DR today and is also 5-band DXCC holder #1. He has remained one of the most dedicated 160-meter operators in the world over the years, with a current 160-Meter DXCC total of over 275 confirmed.

1955

Another memorable year of firsts takes place on Topband. ZLs work into VS6, and ZL/G QSOs become more frequent. New countries active on the band now include HK, HR, OA, OD, TA, and VS6.

Stew Perry's march to DXCC picks up steam this year, as he bags HK4DP. W1BB now reports 28 countries on the band. W9PNE is also doing a fine job from the Midwest at 17. Sadly, DL1FF reports that DL is off the band now and can only listen in.

Bill Leonard, W2SKE, is now active on the band and is reported to have the most consistent signal on Topband into Europe during the 1955 ARRL DX Tests. Bill, it may be remembered, was one of the original mainstays at the famed K2GL/N2AA multi-multi operation over the years and also is remembered as a successful businessman. He was a Senior Vice President of CBS Network News for many years until his retirement in the 1980s. Excitement during the ARRL DX Tests is provided by KL7TM, KG4AB and XE2OK, offering new ones to many of the deserving.

Fig 4-3—Peter Watson, ZL3GQ, in his shack outside Christchurch. Peter's 160-meter signal is well-known worldwide.

Clarry, along with W1BB and G5BY, was a fixture in the early 160-Meter Transatlantic Tests of the 1930s.

Very sadly, the death of a true 160-meter pioneer is reported, as VE1EA passes away this season. Clarry, along with W1BB and G5BY, was a fixture in the early 160-Meter Transatlantic Tests of the 1930s. He achieved many outstanding firsts on the band over his long career, including the amazing QSO with HZ1KE in 1951. VE1EA, who was the "VE1ZZ of his day" on Topband, contributed much to the early history of the band and was well regarded by his peers. The news of his passing was a blow to all who knew him.

After months of skeds, VS6CQ and W6KIP/6 achieve a major first on the band on April 3, 1955, when they finally break through at 1305Z. VS6CQ, transmitting on 2000 kHz and running a mere 10 W, makes the grade to W6 in the first-ever USA/VS6 Topband QSO.

In other news, W4KFC is now up to 21 countries on Topband. On the equipment front, the Collins 75A4 debuts at a price of $695. TMC scores with its fine GPR-90 inhaler and a National

Fig 4-4—The famous ZL3GQ quad and home-brew tower.

NC-300 "Dream Receiver" can be had for $399!

As the 1955 season winds down, Peter Watson, ZL3GQ, appears on the band for the first time, along with FB8XX, ST2NG, ZD3BFC and ZP5GM. Peter Watson, by the way, later produces some of the biggest 160-meter signals ever to come out of ZL, using a 100-foot high flattop dipole. He provides a ZL multiplier and DXCC counter for many in DX contests over the years.

As 1955 comes to a close, W1BB notes that 160 meters seems to be open year round to some part of the world. The only real limiting factor is QRN, which serves to keep summertime QSO counts down. However, on relatively quiet nights, surprisingly good contacts can be made by those who are active and alert on the band. (Even today, how true that statement still is for true-blue Topband believers. There is *always* something doing on 160 meters if you have the perseverance to go after it!)

1956

In a surprise move, effective July 9, 1956, the FCC announces a reorganization of the loran system in the USA. Although promised as a temporary one-year measure, nighttime power levels are reduced to 200 W in many states and to 50 W in others. Most severely impacted are stations in SE Texas, Louisiana, Mississippi, Alabama, Georgia, Florida, Puerto Rico, Virgin Islands, Guam and other US possessions and territories who as of this date no longer have any 160-meter privileges whatsoever. These measures are reported by the US Coast Guard to be the absolute minimum necessary to maintain navigational safety for

Fig 4-5—Ern Orchard, G3PU, in his shack. Ern achieved WAC #2 on 160 meters in 1957.

Fig 4-6—Two of the UK's finest 160-meter operators over the years: Nev Bethune, G3RFS (left) and Keith Spicer, G3RPB (right). Keith is a holder of the 40-Zone WAZ on 160 meters.

the US ships and aircraft that use the loran system. Loran has absolute priority in the 1.8 to 2.0-MHz band.

In spite of this dreadful news, 160 meters otherwise has another great year. In February, newcomer ZL3GQ wastes no time in making the 1.8-MHz grade to VS6CQ. G3PU works ZL1GX, making such antipodal QSOs seem almost routine. W9PNE is now up to a DXCC count of 21 in the heartland, with five counters toward his 160-Meter WAC. DL1FF is back on the band again, as are newcomers 3V8AX and YN1AA.

On February 12, 1956, W1BB scores another first, working HB1CM/HE in Liechtenstein, who transmits on 1769 kHz. (Note that this is outside the USA 160-meter band and that this QSO is the result of split frequency skeds made in advance.) During the summer of 1956 Stew Perry again scores with QSOs to ZS2GE and ZS2KZ. In September, W1BB hits more pay dirt with VP3AD. In December, Stew achieves another first-ever QSO with CP5EQ.

On the equipment front, a Hallicrafters SX-101 inhaler (a fine 160-meter receiver in its day) can be had at year's end for $375. The first Novice WACs are achieved this year: KN6JQJ is #1, followed by WN0ZQV and KN5ALA respectively.

1957

The year starts out famously for G3PU, who in February 1957 achieves his 160-Meter WAC. New on the band are ZB2BJ and PY2AJK. In March, W1BB scores with VP2LU. In April, G3PU achieves a magnificent contact with AC5PN.

In May, W1BB achieves two more first-ever QSOs with TG9AD and ZB1HKO in Malta. Also in May on the equipment front, the Collins KWM-1 debuts with a rather healthy price tag for its day of $770.

In August 1957, Charlie O'Brien, W2EQS, and W1BB score with FP8AA and FP8AS respectively. Newcomer VR3A is QRV on the band and looking for QSOs. At the other end of the frequency spectrum, history is being made of near epic proportions. On July 8, 1957, John, W6NLZ, and Ralph "Tommy" Thomas, KH6UK, (ex W2UK) achieve the first-ever QSO between the mainland US and Hawaii—at the unbelievable frequency of 144 MHz! This feat will later be repeated on even-higher frequency VHF bands by this dedicated duo. (It should be noted that Tommy Thomas was also an accomplished DXer and contester in addition to his VHF prowess. As W2UK he was the top USA scorer on CW in the ARRL DX Tests conducted in 1937 and 1938, the first back-to-back wins ever achieved by a US entrant.)

1958

Many additional firsts occur this year. W6KIP works KP6AL. W1BB begins receiving UA1 SWL cards and works VP7BT and VP9EP. W4KFC makes the grade with KH6IJ and HH2KVU. VK2AGH and ZL5AC (Antarctica) are active on the band. On the darker side, the US loses its allocation at 1875 to 2000 kHz temporarily.

In a sign of much bigger things to come, Scott Redd, KØDQI, achieves DXCC as a 13 year old. He wonders if he is the youngest ever to make the grade. Not quite, as 12-year old Bill Tippett, KN4RID, operating from North Carolina, works 116 DXCC counters during the 1957 to 1958 solar maximum and becomes the first Novice holder of DXCC in late 1958. That youngster, KN4RID (later WØZV and now W4ZV—see Fig 4-7) achieved his DXCC using a Viking Ranger, a Collins 75A4 receiver and a

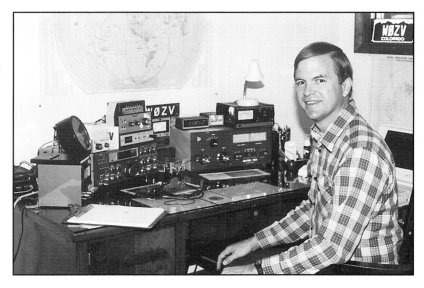

Fig 4-7—Bill Tippett, WØZV (now W4ZV) in his Colorado shack. He now operates from North Carolina as W4ZV and has confirmed over 285 countries on Topband! Bill also achieved the first-ever all-Novice DXCC in 1958 as KN4RID.

Fig 4-8—Peter Bobek, DJ8WL, in his shack. Peter also holds the prestigious 40-Zone WAZ award on 160 meters.

Fig 4-9—DJ8WL inverted-L 160-meter transmitting antenna.

Fig 4-10—A few of DJ8WL's best 160-meter QSLs. A number of these would be outstanding catches even on 20-meter SSB!

Telrex two-element tribander at approximately 50 feet. Using four low-end 15-meter crystals wrapped in tape for quick QSY and rotating his antenna via the "armstrong method," Bill accomplished his feat well within the one-year Novice licensee period. Although others may have worked over 100 countries as one-year Novices, only KN4RID, KN1IVT, KNØLTB and WN8TND are known to have actually applied for and received ARRL DXCC-Desk authenticated one-year Novice century-club awards. Well done, men!

KØDQI later goes on to become a highly successful DXer and contester, operating from XE1IIJ, W3GRF and A92Q. K4RID/WØZV/W4ZV discovers 160 meters around 1983 and goes on to become one of the finest 160-meter DXers ever to play the game, with a current 160-Meter DXCC confirmed total of over 285 countries.

On the equipment front, a Heathkit DX-40 can be had for $64.95 and its big brother, the DX-100 is available for $189.95. Of course, you do have to assemble these kits to get them on the air!

Fig 4-11—DJ8WL with Deitmar, DL3DXX (left) and Rudi, DJ5CQ (right), of VK9CR, Cocos, and VK9XY, Christmas Island, DXpedition fame.

$\overline{1959}$

Active and reported on Topband are UB5EP, UB5FJ, UA3BS, UA9CM, HB9NL, VQ2GR, VS1EB and ZE3JO. TF2WCC in Iceland listens in as well. W1BB scores with a QSO to ZL3RB. ZL3RB hears VP7BT but does not complete a QSO in May. 16-year old Peter Bobek, DJ8WL, begins listening in on Topband with a two-tube receiver and copies G and OK stations. Many years later, this fine operator will achieve 160-Meter DXCC #33, the eighth in Europe and a 40-zone WAZ on Topband.

Chapter 5

160-Meter DXing Chronology, 1960 To 1969

1960

Newcomers on the band include EL4A (W7VCB), OD5LX running 450 W and 5A2CV. On the equipment front, the Gonset GSB-101 debuts and can be had for $459.50.

1961

This is a banner year for W1BB, as he works HH2V, UB5WF and EL4A early in the year for countries #55 to 57. In March, W8GDQ works ZC4AK and completes his WAC on 160 meters, #3 after W1BB and G3PU. As of July 1961 G3PU reports a DXCC count of 38; W9PNE has reached the 33 level and ZC4AK reports 14 DXCC counters on 160 meters in four WAC continents.

In late spring 1961, W1PPN makes the grade on 1876 kHz to ZL3RB at 1018Z. In December, Dana Atchley, W1HKK, (later W1CF), shows up on the band and scores with SSB QSOs to G3FPQ and G3CHN around 1803 kHz at 0100 Z. (The team of W1CF and Fred Collins, W1FC, later develops the highly effective Four-Square vertical array, an antenna now quite popular among Topband DXers.) David Courtier-Dutton, G3FPQ, is still very active on 160 meters to this date and consistently has one of the finer signals out of Europe on the band.

SWL Tyndall in Vermont has received and confirmed 123 countries on the AM broadcast band during this same time. Listener Stanbury of Ontario has 86. A Maryland SWL enthusiast named Holbrook claims confirmed reception of 35 countries on frequencies *below* 550 kHz.

1962

Another big year for 160 meters unfolds as W1BB works VP8GQ in the South Orkneys. The VP8GQ operator is none other than G3LET, who is with the British Antarctic Survey. VP8GQ is also worked shortly thereafter by WØIFH and a little-known newcomer, VE1ZZ. Students of 160 meters later get to know this fine fellow very well indeed as "Jack" Leahy soon establishes himself as one of the fixtures on 160 meters. Following in the footsteps of Clarry, VE1EA, and today using a fine Four-Square array of inverted-L antennas, Jack continues to make QSOs others thought impossible on the band. His current 160-meter total is now close to 280 confirmed and includes the first long-path QSOs ever made between North America and Japan. Jack achieves this feat for the first time in December 1995, and repeats it several times later that same month and again in January 1996!

Fig 5-1—Jack Leahy, VE1ZZ, in his Nova Scotia shack. One of the "160-meter Beacon" signals, Jack consistently makes QSOs others thought impossible on Topband!

Other notable QSOs include Gs working into VE3BQL/SU. FB8BX reports hearing W1RAN, Ned Raub, in Connecticut along with EI, G, GW and five US call areas. In late February 1962, VE1ZZ completes a stunning QSO with EP2BK, who is none other than WØGTA/LA2YH. Bob at EP2BK reports that he is using a Collins 32V-2 transmitter and an old AR-88 receiver. W1BB and W2IU also make the 1.8-MHz grade to EP2BK in March.

In July, VP8GQ scores again with VE3GP plus W1BB, W2KQT, W3GQF and VE3QU. In September, W2FYT works VK3AKR for another fine East Coast QSO to the land down under. Other stations new to the band include HI8XAG, HK1QQ, HR3HH and UO5AA.

1963

W1BB scores a beauty with a two-way to Martin, OY7ML, for another new one. Armin, DL1FF, now back on the band with gusto, reports a 160-Meter DXCC count of 35 after adding VP8GQ and 5B4GF. W6KIP (now operating using call sign W6ML) reports an April QSO with ZS2FM. There are scads of ZSs active on the band this year, along with ZE3JO.

On July 28, 1963, Stew Perry scores big again when he works K1KSH/KG6 on Marcus Island (Minami Torishima) at 0920 Z. This is a remarkable first-ever QSO from the East Coast of the USA and the closest W1BB ever comes to working Japan on Topband during his glorious run. The QSL sent by W1BB to K1KSH confirming this remarkable QSO has been framed and is memorialized at ARRL HQ in Newington, Connecticut. It was given to General Manager K1ZZ at League Headquarters as a gift and now hangs proudly in the hallway on the second floor.

Later that same year in September, W1BB reaches #79 on Topband by working Mike, 5N2JKO. Other stations active on the band in 1963 include VR3O, SVØWZ, ZE8JJ, ZK1BS, 5B4PB, PZ1AR, CT1CO, GI6TK, many KL7s, SP3RH and ZB1BX.

Although little noted at the time, an 18-year-old James "Ernie" Hemingway, K1PBW, begins operating on the band this season from his summer home on the edge of Long Island Sound in Madison, Connecticut. Running 10 W into a homebrew 2E26 transmitter and using a 300-foot long-wire for an antenna, Ernie

Fig 5-2—"Ernie" Hemingway, K1PBW, at the controls of VP2KC in 1979. Ernie is remembered for his Beverage work, his achievement of 160-Meter DXCC #5 and a superb effort in 1979 on 160 meters from VP2KC during the CQ WW SSB contest.

soon acquires friends all over the East Coast on Topband. These humble beginnings soon lead Ernie to develop one of the finest stations ever assembled on 160 meters and he is rewarded with Topband DXCC #5 in 1976. Ernie's many achievements on 1.8 MHz will be described in more detail later.

Effective June 30, 1963, the FCC "lorans" the US 160-meter frequency allocations yet again, this time reducing the nighttime power levels to 25 or 50 W in many states. Nearly every area of the country is affected in some manner by the new changes.

1964

In April, W1BB does it again, this time with a QSO to 9A1VU in San Marino. Stew also reports working 137 different DX stations in 24 countries during the 1963 to 1964 season. During the summer months Stew connects again, this time with VQ2AS, ZS6BCT, 9L1HX and ZS4PB. It should be noted that Peter Botha, ZS4PB, becomes a fixture on the band thereafter, producing one of the biggest signals out of South Africa on Topband year after year.

In other news, W9PNE reports a fine March 1964 QSO with VK5KO, his #39 on Topband. Also very active on the band now is VS1LP, who in June works JA6AA. On November 12, 1964, W6GTI scores a major first as he achieves the first-ever USA/JA QSO on Topband. This causes increased interest in the band in JA, which had an allocation around 1880 kHz at the time. Some of the early JA pioneers active on the band in 1964 include

Fig 5-3—*Active since before WW II, Brice Anderson, W9PNE, in his Lancaster, Illinois, shack. Brice was one of the early players on 160 meters and has been very successful from the US Midwest.*

Fig 5-4—*Isaji Shima, JA3AA, one of the early 160-meter players from Japan.*

Fig 5-5—*Kuny Togashi, JA7NI, another prominent early JA 160-meter operator.*

JA1CNE, JA1CO, JA2JM, JA2JW, JA2WB, JA2YT, JA3AA, and JA6AK.

JA6AK, Ikuo, rapidly develops into a fine 160-meter DXer running 380 W into a 70-foot vertical. At the end of the year, Ikuo works DL1FF and OK1ZQ for his first two Europeans and is feverishly looking for USA QSOs on 1880 kHz by both long and short paths at 2140 Z and 1100 Z respectively. (Hmm...Ikuo should have tried making a schedule with Jack, VE1ZZ, who was the first to make a long-path QSO with JA some 31 years later.)

Others heard on the band include HP1IE, KR6BQ, OE3JL, OX3DL, UA3KAA, UA0KBB, UB5FJ, UO5AA, VK9GL, ZS9G, 3A2BZ, 5Z4IV, 6YAXG in Jamaica, 9J2AS, 9G1DV, and 9M4LP. K1PBW, now shunt feeding his dad's old 50-foot TV tower as a loaded vertical, works his first Gs on the band as the year commences and becomes thoroughly hooked by the DX bug on Topband.

1965

This is an extraordinary season on 160 meters. It starts off well for W1BB as he works Robert, ZP9AY, on January 11, 1965, at 0616 Z for #84. Robert had heard Stew during the previous summer months but could not get through. This is followed up quickly in late January with a QSO to Peter, ZB2AE (G3MRE), for Stew's #85.

During the CQ 160-Meter CW Test of 1965 it is reported that daytime propagation on 160 meters can be pretty spectacular. QSOs between well-equipped stations at distances up to 1000 miles are commonplace. G3PU reports hearing W1BB/1 until 0930 local time on January 24, 1965. Later that same day, Stew works VO1FB at 1950 Z. A couple of weeks later, VO1FB works G3GRS and G3SRC as early as 1910 Z.

Other contest QSOs include newcomer JA6AK working 9M4LP (ex-VS1LP). Ikuo also heard but did not work W6RW, W7VGQ, VK5KO and 9L1HX. DL1FF makes the grade with HK4EB. G2PL also works 9M4LP. G3PU reports hearing W6RW from 0645 to 0745 Z RST 569, better than most East Coast stations. Roger Mace, W6RW, develops into a truly dedicated 160-meter DXer and achieves the first 160-meter USA West Coast DXCC on the band, #25, on April 11, 1983.

Frequent SSB QSOs are now reported between the USA East Coast and VK. VS1LP manages an SSB two-way with VK3ATN. GM3IGW makes the grade to 9M4LP, while G3PU reports an SSB QSO with ZL3RB. W9PNE is now reporting 40 DXCC countries worked, an excellent total from the Midwest. K5JVF works VP2VL, his #15 on Topband.

While 160-meter DXing is a relatively simple matter and almost becoming ho-hum for some, Peter at VP3CZ reports that he must completely assemble and disassemble his entire rig and antenna each time he operates 160 meters! Another Peter, G3JBR, reports that after two years of trying, he finally managed to work W1BB/1 and VO1FB. Peter was using 10 W to an 80-foot antenna with counterpoise. Now that's dedication for you.

Fig 5-6—Two of the "best of the West," Roger Mace, W6RW (left), and Earl Cunningham, K6SE (right). Roger and Earl are remembered as the "Left Coast" 160-Meter DXCC holders #1 and #2, and #25 and 55 overall in the DXCC standings.

Fig 5-7—David Wilson, G3SZA (left), first European 160-Meter DXCC holder and #16 overall with Tom Rauch, W8JI (right). Tom is well known among 160-meter DXers for his antenna knowledge and overall technical expertise.

Some familiar friends from the 1990s are heard on the band this year, including WA8IJI. Tom is still quite active today on 160 meters as W8JI. Also making quite a splash is HI8XAL, Fred Laun, who is better known today as K3ZO. SWL Rolf Rasp, later to achieve the first 160-Meter DXCC from South America and #14 overall as PY1RO, visits the states to take a computer course and buy a competition grade receiver for 160 meters. Herb Schoenbohm, WØVXO, becomes quite active on 160 meters this season. He will later achieve 160-Meter DXCC #4 operating from KV4FZ. Sadly, Grand Old Man of 160 meters Harry Merriman, G6GM, is remembered posthumously by his friends on the band.

On the equipment front, the Collins KWM-2 arrives on the scene for $1150. A Drake TR-4 is available for $585 and Hy-Gain antennas sports an interesting rotatable pole called the RP100 complete with their famous Long-John Yagis for 40 through 10 meters. Barry Goldwater, K7UGA, has one of the first of these standing tall in his backyard. The AMECO nuvistor preamp is now available, complete with an internal power supply for $32.95. This becomes quite a popular little device, as 160-meter DXers learn that a Beverage's performance can be enhanced dramatically with one of these in the line ahead of the receiver.

At the other end of the spectrum, moonbounce tests are conducted from July 3 to July 24, 1965, on 432 MHz using the famous 1000-foot dish antenna at Arecibo, Puerto Rico. Some 28 QSOs are made into the USA and Europe during the tests. One of them is with Ralph Green, W1HGT, who will later achieve 160-Meter DXCC #2 following W1BB.

A general band plan has emerged on Topband and is well understood by savvy 160-meter ops: East Coast stations congregate from 1800 to 1825 kHz. West Coast stations can be found from 1975 to 2000 kHz. VKs congregate from 1800 to 1860 kHz. ZLs seem to like 1875 to 1900 kHz. JAs abound around 1880 kHz.

1966

Ralph Green, W1HGT, is now on the band in earnest and has begun his march toward 160-Meter DXCC #2. He notes: "I became interested in Topband shortly after receiving my engineering degree in college. I had been fairly active on the other

Fig 5-8—Herb Schoenbohm, KV4FZ, holder of 160-Meter DXCC #4, in his shack with Lloyd and Iris Colvin, W6KG and W6QL.

bands, and while it had been fun chasing DX there, it was losing its challenge. It just did not seem to have that much appeal to me after some time and while I don't exactly know why, I guess I was looking for different kinds of things to make my operating more interesting again. I had tried VHF DXing, and while that was also quite interesting to me, there you have to be prepared for all sorts of battles with your neighbors over TVI etc. So, I then decided to try the other end of the spectrum and that's how 160 meters came into play for me—partially because of the propagation aspects, and partially because of the regulatory aspects which limited the scope of operating on 160 meters; eg, the power levels, the frequency allocations permitted and the small number of DXCC countries available on 160 meters. Other factors like "grayline" also intrigued me. Before long, I also found I liked even the *kind* of amateurs I found on 160 meters. They did not seem to be as obsessed with things as the operators on the higher bands seemed to be and I soon found myself very much at home on 1.8 MHz!"

In June 1966, W1BB makes another first-ever QSO, this time with CX3BH. Sadly, DXpeditioners ZL2AWJ and K7LMU are killed at sea in a typhoon on January 27, 1966, while sailing their ketch from Wallis Island to Apia, Samoa. Lloyd and Iris Colvin, W6KG and WB6QEP (W6QL), are active in the Pacific and Europe, making over 30,000 QSOs in 1966. Jim Lawson, W2PV (then WA2SFP), is active on Topband in DX contests, with quite a signal reported in Europe.

W1BB embarks on an Asian cruise from September 10, 1966, to February 1, 1967. After crossing the Pacific, he listens in from Japan using an R-4A and a $1/4$-wavelength wire. He reports hearing W6HRG, WØVXO, VE7AKI and KL7FRY. JAs are now clustered in a new allocation at 1907.5 to 1912.5 kHz. Stew reports that QSOs from JA to the USA East Coast will be difficult indeed, since commercial stations blanket 1.800 to 1.804 MHz over there.

Interesting first-ever QSOs are reported between KL7FRY (K6SE) and JA1PVK/ZL3RB. W8JIN now reports 28 countries on 160 meters. Special "First Timers" Transatlantic Tests are announced on the band to give lesser-equipped stations a shot at DX. These are planned for January 8 and March 5, 1966, from 0500 to 0730 Z. On his return trip from the Far East, W1BB hears many W6s and W7s, plus W5YXG, W9PAW, WØPSF/Ø and WØGDH.

1967

Ernie, K1PBW, rediscovers and reintroduces the Beverage receiving antenna almost by accident. The manner in which it occurred makes a fascinating story. Ernie was experimenting with a 1100-foot Beverage after reading about the original efforts of Harold Beverage conducted for RCA at station WCC on Cape Cod, Massachusetts. Initially, Ernie was trying to use the Beverage as a transmitting antenna directed S/SW. He had dismal results and was about to abandon the project. As luck would have it, Jan, DL9KR, made an expedition late in 1967 to CEØ. Precisely on schedule at 0600 Z, using the Beverage for receiving Ernie hears CEØPC fire up on 1.827 MHz at RST 569. All the big guns begin calling Jan on 1.801 to 1.804 MHz, with many sending reports, believing they have made valid QSOs.

Hearing CEØPC solidly, Ernie realized he had stumbled onto a *major* find. While his Beverage was a lousy transmitting antenna, it was an *excellent* receiving antenna! Ernie began calling CEØPC and eventually made his QSO when it became obvious that no one else was really copying Jan's signal that first night. Jan, running 25 W into a crystal-controlled transmitter, later confirms K1PBW as his only US contact on 160 meters that evening among three QSOs total. The other two QSOs were made with South American stations.

In the roundtable that ensued following that 0600 to 0700 Z vigil, the Beverage receiving antenna became an instant celebrity. The next day found almost every serious Topband DXer stringing out reels of wire to the southwest, some over real estate that they owned; others over neighbors' front yards and city streets, clandestinely using #24 enameled wire if the neighborhood nearby was an unfriendly one. The age of the 160-meter receiving antenna had begun!

While his Beverage was a lousy transmitting antenna, it was an excellent receiving antenna!

Fig 5-9—John, G3PQA (top right), along with some very fine 160-meter company. From left to right, top row: G4AKY, G3SZA, G3PQA. Bottom row: PAØHIP, 4X4NJ, G4AAW.

On the transmitting antenna front, KL7FRY in the Aleutians reports using 800 and 2000-foot longwires to hunt for East Coast stations on 1.803 MHz. WØVXO employs a 136-foot vertical with 50 radials. This helps explain his great success from the Midwest.

Japanese ops have really taken to their new segment above 1900 kHz. They reported many QSOs with W6s, KL7FRY, VE7AKI and 9V1LP. Most active are JA1BHG, JA1PVK, JA3AA and JA3JM. JAs report a burning desire to work the USA East Coast on 160 meters, but the first QSOs into the W2 US district will have to wait until February 2, 1981, when Bill, K2GNC, scores with JA6ITF at 1120 Z. These are followed in quick succession by QSOs with JA6LCJ and JH6OFC. JA6IEF and JA2GQO are also heard but not worked due to QRM.

John, G3PQA, is now active on Topband and reports that 320-kV UK power grids badly trash 1.8-MHz reception in England. Newcomer Pedro Piza, KP4AST (NP4A), is now active on the band from his mountaintop QTH near Ponce.

Fig 5-10—K1PBW's QTH in western Massachusetts, showing his very fine phased vertical array. Ernie's signal in Europe was outstanding from this QTH in the woods.

A remarkable first is achieved by W2RAA on September 12, 1967, when he works VQ8CCR on Rodriguez at 2300 Z. Steve, GU3MS, then with International Aeradio, is reported to be the operator at the Indian Ocean end. VK5KO also manages a QSO.

In November 1967, K1PBW and others, as noted above, manage to work CEØPC operated by DL9KR. For Charlie, W2EQS, it is his #55 on 160 meters. Once again, the FCC issues revised allocations for 160 meters although, this time, the changes imposed are less upsetting than previous announcements.

1968

As the year starts, W1BB is nearing the 100-country mark. K1PBW, flushed with his success with CEØPC, has now installed five more Beverages at his Mount Carmel, Connecticut, QTH. The longest of these is a real beauty—1600 feet in length aimed toward Europe. About this antenna Ernie reports: "I owe much of my DXing success to variations on the Beverage antenna, which I never used for transmitting purposes again. If you look at the CQ

Fig 5-11—Two of the UK's very best 160-meter signals come from Roger, G3RBP (left) and Don, G3XTT (right).

160-Meter contest results from 1968 on, you can appreciate the results. I worked more Europeans than most everyone else combined and this was solely because I could *hear them*. And the Europeans knew it. I can remember hearing a hive of wobbly European signals desperately calling me as sunrise swept across their land. I could even hear stations in Europe that Western Europeans could not hear. Wherever I operated from after 1968, I always took the Beverage antenna with me in some form or another as it was a real performer!"

In the Midwest, Herb, WØVXO, is now at about 40 countries on 160 meters, having added CEØPC, PZ1AH, TGØAA and 6W8CW. On January 28, 1968, ARRL President, WØNWX, worked KA9MF on 1.880/1.998 MHz for his WAC. Bob is active later this same year from VP2VL, a precursor to his current call sign in retirement, VP2VI. Also in the Midwest, W9PNE gets KA9AK on March 8, 1968, for his WAC.

Later in the season, WØVXO, QSYs to Colorado operating portable zero, working many JAs and even switching over to SSB on his side for some unique cross-mode QSOs. In the fall, Herb discovers the magic of the Caribbean on 160 meters and lays plans for his December 1968 move to KV4FZ.

I can remember hearing a hive of wobbly European signals desperately calling me as sunrise swept across their land.

Fig 5-12—Roger, G3UPK (and ZB2AY), at ST2AY. Roger is well known on 160 meters today as VK4YB.

Fig 5-13—The fabulous lighthouse QTH of GW3UUZ, "Andy the Lamp."

In late spring, W1BB nets ZC4RP and 5Z4LE. Finally, in August 1968, Stew reaches the 100 mark, with receipt of a QSL from CE3CZ. However, three of these are for pre-1945 country QSOs. Thus, Stew elects to continue the hunt a while longer to secure several more postwar DXCC counters.

A number of well known calls begin frequenting the band about this time. Don Field, G3XTT, begins to take an interest in 160 and Roger Parsons, G3RBP, has already established a presence on 1.8 MHz. (Later, Don and Roger edit and produce a successor to the *160-Meter Topband Newsletter*, having taken it over from Ivan Payne, VE3DO, who had picked it up when W1BB could no longer continue producing it about 1982.)

The FCC once again announces new loran A changes. The bad news is that a new loran signal is being added at 1900 kHz. The good news is that most areas will not lose privileges. In a few states, a full kW is anticipated in one 25-kHz segment.

1969

Arnold Tamchin, W2HCW, returns from Japan this year and plans a major antenna farm on Long Island, NY. Naturally, it includes first-class antennas for Topband, where Arnold later has a massive signal, mainly on SSB.

Herb, now WØVXO/KV4, begins his run from St Croix. This will culminate in his receiving 160-Meter DXCC #4 on November 3, 1976. Dick Gibson, GI3OQR, is heard often on the band now. He will later receive 160-Meter DXCC #28, the sixth from Europe, on September 28, 1983.

Although largely preoccupied with helping XYL Alice recover from heart troubles, W1BB gets on enough in January to be copied in Japan by JA2CLI on January 26, 1969. No two-way QSO is made, however. Stew loses part of his famous V Beam in a severe winter storm in New England.

Roger, G3UPK, is active on the band at ZB2AY. He will later become better known as ST2AY and VK4YB, his current call in Queensland. Also active this year are Charles, YV1OB, and Gus Browning at 6W/W4BPD.

A couple of timely DXpeditions helped push W1BB over the top. Stew works VP2KK (who made 28 Topband QSOs) and HKØTU (who made 52 Topband QSOs) for a legitimate postwar W1BB DXCC. During the HKØ chase, Stew reportedly has a bad piece of coax in his receiver line that he located and repaired just in time to make the QSO.

This ends the 39-year effort by Stew Perry, begun around 1930, to achieve his goal of confirming 100 countries on Topband. At the time it should again be noted, there was no specific single-band 160-Meter DXCC award available for Stew to apply for. He could only submit QSLs for a general DXCC award, which in his case, would have been a Mixed DXCC award. Stew elected *not* to apply for a mixed DXCC award and chose instead just to savor his success after the long quest.

By October 1976, which is when the single-band 160-Meter DXCC award actually became available, a number of other 160-meter DXers had also managed to confirm 100 countries on

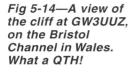

Fig 5-14—A view of the cliff at GW3UUZ, on the Bristol Channel in Wales. What a QTH!

Fig 5-15—Aki, JA5DQH, and his famous call sign license-plate collection. Aki is also well known for his work from HI8A.

Fig 5-16—The very FB shack of Kinji Makino, JA2GQO, JA and Asia 160-Meter DXCC #2 and #76 overall.

Fig 5-17—The JA2GQO 160-meter antenna, a full-sized loop.

Topband. Given that situation, one might imagine someone else happening, by chance or otherwise, to apply for a 160-Meter DXCC award ahead of W1BB, thus achieving certificate #1 from the League.

Fortunately, and true to the spirit of the "Gentleman's Band," those who also achieved 100 countries between 1969 and 1976, decided informally among them—selves that a distinct pecking order be observed. According to K1PBW, it was agreed that those having achieved 100 countries from 1969 to 1976 should file for their awards in the same relative order in which they were actually achieved. Thus W1BB would get his richly deserved certificate #1, W1HT would receive #2, W8LRL would receive #3 and KV4FZ would receive #4. In October 1976 those were, most likely, the only actual holders of 100 QSLs. Ernie, K1PBW, was very close but did not receive his 100th QSL until early in 1977.

This was in keeping with history as it should have been written. To their credit, the 160-meter operators of the day ensured that W1BB's place as #1 might be preserved. Actually, we know that W1HT and W1BB filed *together* and Ralph expressed clearly that he should receive 160-Meter DXCC #2, following Stew, since that was the way it had actually happened.

Thus ends the story of W1BB's remarkable achievement of the first-ever 160-Meter DXCC, but not this chronology. Many significant happenings continued to occur on 1.8 MHz that deserve mention in these pages, albeit in a more abbreviated form.

In the August 1969 issue, *QST* ran an interesting picture of the lighthouse QTH of Andy Bluer, GW3UUZ. Located directly on the coast near Cardiff, Wales, where he is known affectionately as "Andy the Lamp," Andy's QTH resembles the UK version of the W1BB water-tower site at Point Shirley. With a

Fig 5-18—Famous Israeli DXer and contester Riki Kline, 4X4NJ. Riki has earned the most difficult WAS award, has confirmed 40-Zone WAZ on 160 meters and has provided many 160-meter operators with their Asian counter for 160-meter WAC.

homebrew rig, an HQ-170 receiver and wires suspended from the top of the 180-foot lighthouse on a cliff 100 feet above the Bristol channel, Andy was reported to have an enormous 160-meter signal. Some 21 years later, I stumbled upon this spot on a vacation trip through the vale of Glamorgan. I said something to the effect: "Man! This would be one *superb* location for a 160-meter DXer." Little was known at the time of its fine history under GW3UUZ!

On the opposite side of the world, some well-known JAs are just getting started making their runs toward the first JA 160-Meter DXCC. Among this select group are JA7AO, JA3ONB, JA5DQH, JA2GQO and JA6LCJ. In what becomes a nail-biting shoot-out over 16 years, Aki, JA5DQH, achieves JA DXCC #1, first Asia and #75 overall on March 4, 1985. Countryman Kinji Makino, JA2GQO, is second by *one day*, achieving ARRL accreditation on March 5, 1985. In a remarkable twist, Riki Kline, 4X4NJ, receives DXCC #77 on March 5, 1985, also just behind JA2GQO. One can appreciate the intensity with which the first Asian 160-Meter DXCC was contested across some 8000 miles. It was a close one indeed, with JA5DQH winning a squeaker! Except for JA2GQO, who retired from 160-meter DXing around 1986, all of these fine amateurs can still be found on Topband today in the 1990s.

Chapter 6

160-Meter DXing Chronology, 1970 to 1979

In this period, Wally Eckles, WB8APH (later W8LRL), in West Virginia takes an interest in the band. Assembling a superb station just west of Baltimore in nearby Charles Town, West Virginia, Wally makes his presence known in short order. Using a vertical with many radials, numerous Beverages and blessed with a quiet receiving location, Wally quickly becomes one of the leaders on Topband. He achieves DXCC #3 after W1BB and W1HGT on November 2, 1976. Along the way, he picks up a new call, W8LRL, and becomes active in all 160-meter contests until about

Fig 6-1—Wally Eckles, W8LRL, 160-Meter DXCC holder #3, standing next to his 1/4-wave vertical antenna. Wally has provided West Virginia to many of the 160-meter deserving over the years.

Fig 6-2—A close-up of one of W8LRL's two-wire Beverages.

1983. The sudden death of his wife and an illness later slow him down a bit around 1992. This fine gentleman can still be found on the band from time to time chasing the occasional new one.

Others deserving mention around this time include Earl Cunningham, W5RTQ (K6SE). Using a pair of phased shunt-fed towers from his Palmdale, California QTH, Earl achieves West Coast DXCC #2 after W6RW on May 2, 1984, and #55 overall.

Jack Wheeler, KH6CHC, is very active about this time operating from Pupukea on the island of Oahu. He can often be heard at 1.997 MHz listening around 1.803 MHz. Jack, who is better known today as KH6CC, is just about everyone's Hawaii for WAS on 160 meters. He now lives on the big island of Hawaii, moving there to get more land and a bit of relief from nearby contester KH6XX on Oahu.

Jack's new place on the Big Island of Hawaii is a 160-meter DXer's dream QTH. It is a large parcel away from the coast and free from all man-made utilities and noise. Jack runs his entire home and most of his station on solar power. When he hears

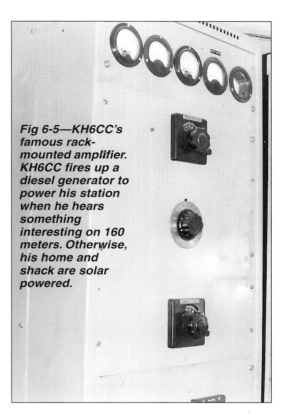

Fig 6-5—KH6CC's famous rack-mounted amplifier. KH6CC fires up a diesel generator to power his station when he hears something interesting on 160 meters. Otherwise, his home and shack are solar powered.

Fig 6-3—Earl Cunningham, K6SE (ex W5RTQ/KL7FRY), a stalwart 160-meter West Coast operator and holder of DXCC #55, stands next to his 160-meter antenna in Palmdale, California.

Fig 6-4—Everybody's KH6, Jack Wheeler, KH6CC, in his shack on the Big Island of Hawaii.

Fig 6-8—Well-known 160-meter DXer Willem, PAØHIP, with his XYL Francis.

Fig 6-6—The KH6CC $\frac{1}{4}$-wave 160-meter vertical.

Fig 6-7—Rolf Rasp, PY1RO, in his shack outside Rio de Janeiro, Brazil. Rolf is remembered for achieving the first 160-Meter DXCC outside North America, #14 overall.

Fig 6-9—The PA0HIP ham shack. Willem achieved the second 160-Meter DXCC in Europe, following G3SZA. He always has a terrific Topband signal!

Fig 6-10—Barry Boothe, W9UCW, and his XYL Joyce. Barry is remembered for his fine 160-meter signal from Illinois and for his work with the "Minooka Special" 160-meter antenna.

Fig 6-11—Some of the crew at VP2KC. From left to right: N4NX, K1PBW, VP2KC, N4PN, N4RJ. Ernie, K1PBW, looks "beat" because he just finished erecting the 160-meter vertical.

Fig 6-12—The fine 160-meter vertical at VP2KC in 1979. Man, did this antenna play! 526 QSOs, 11 Zones and 47 Countries on 160-meter SSB in the 1979 CQ WW *Phone contest.*

something of interest on Topband, he simply fires up his diesel generator, which then generates power for the exciter, a TS-830S and his kW amplifier. Jack, a ham for over 60 years now, built his amplifier just after WW II and it is a rack-mounted beauty. It sure pokes out a great signal to a $^1/_4$-wave vertical sitting above an elaborate, elevated radial system supported by 15-foot tall railroad ties.

SWL Rolf Rasp, having graduated to amateur status as PY1RO, became very active during this period. Rolf achieves the first DXCC outside North America and #14 overall on July 18, 1979.

David Wilson, G3SZA, is also a fixture on the band in this period and achieves the first European DXCC on 160 meters, #16 overall, on March 3, 1980. He is followed shortly thereafter by Willem, PA0HIP; Mike, GD4BEG; Keith, G3RPB; Jarda, OK1ATP and Dick, GI3OQR in that order.

Barry Boothe, W9UCW, of Minooka, Illinois (one of the few who kept the Midwest alive in the 1970s), is also very active on Topband in these years. He is known for his work on a shortened vertical for 160 meters known as the "Minooka Special." Barry is also remembered for his pioneering work on two-wire Beverages for 160 meters, as his design was quite popular at the time. It is rumored that Barry can be found today in South Texas with a 160-meter horizontal loop at 50 feet for an antenna. Lately he supports XYL WB9NUL's addiction to county hunting and enjoys woodworking.

Also active in this period is Tom, W8JI, operating from Ohio. Among Tom's many fine achievements are some of the easternmost QSOs made on 160 meters with Japan *before* the shutdown of loran. Some very fine listening techniques made these contacts possible. Tom remains active on 160 meters from Georgia these days and is well-known for his technical expertise on antennas, transmission lines and construction practices.

In 1979, a major multi-multi effort is planned by Paul Newberry, N4PN, and others for the *CQ* WW Phone DX Test from VP2KC in the Caribbean. This takes place at "Kit" Carson's Ottley's Estate on St Kitts. As the team is assembled, Ernie, K1PBW, is asked to be the 160-meter band captain.

Over the course of the summer and fall of 1979, Ernie travels to St Kitts several times on Kit's private plane to erect a full sized ¼-wave vertical for 160 meters and three remote-controlled Beverages up in the jungle behind the station. In the weeks leading up to contest time, Kit's staff buries *miles* of copper radials beneath the vertical to increase its effectiveness.

During the contest itself, conditions are relatively poor on 160 meters, as it is a sunspot-maximum year. Nevertheless Ernie, operating with Steve Reichlyn, AA4V, manages to make 526 QSOs, 11 zones and 47 countries from the Caribbean on SSB. At the time, this was an *enormous* score, since most of the US multi-multis of the period would usually net less than 100 QSOs, 5 to 7 zones and perhaps 20 countries on Topband!

Ernie and Steve managed to work many Russians on SSB during the test and were reported to be heard with a steady S7 signal all night long in New Zealand, from just after ZL sunset until well after VP2 sunrise. The overall effort on all bands sets a new World Record in the Multi-Multi class. This was a remarkable achievement from North America, where USA QSOs are valued at only two points each.

Ernie regarded this effort as the high point of his Topband career and retired from 160-meter DXing two years later. He noted that, for him at least, there was little else left to achieve on the band in his time. He would leave it to others, in their time, to push the 160-meter DX envelope farther.

Chapter 7

160-Meter DXing Chronology, 1980 to 1989

A momentous event, the cessation of loran-A operation on 1900 kHz occurs. Immediately thereafter, USA Midwest stations begin hearing and working JA stations with relative ease. Jon Zaimes, AA1K, is now on the band operating from Connecticut and scores a super QSO with VS6DO.

Fig 7-1—Jon Zaimes, AA1K (right) with Dave Wilson, G3SZA (AA0RS). Jon now lives near Wilmington, Delaware.

On May 21, 1981, more wonderful news is revealed when the FCC lifts most USA restrictions in the 1800 to 1900-kHz range. Kilowatt power levels are authorized, both day and night, for the first time. Only 1900 to 2000 kHz is partially restricted by power level because Canadian loran has not yet shut down and still must be protected.

It is reported that on January 1, 1982, a new JA subband will be authorized, CW only, from 1810 to 1825 kHz. The range from 1907.5 to 1912.5 kHz is supposed to be phased out shortly thereafter. For unknown reasons, licensing details are never worked out and to this day, JAs remain in the upper allocation only. This makes 160-meter DXing most difficult for JA ops, since nearly all QSOs must be made split. Thus the achievement of a 160-Meter DXCC from Japan continues to rank among the most difficult accomplishments possible on Topband, as can be seen from the dearth of 200-country DXCC holders from JA.

Arch Doty, K8CFU, is remembered during this period for his pioneering work on the use of elevated radials in 160-meter vertical systems. One of the first to realize that the use of elevated radials reduces the *number* of radials required, Arch published his findings in order that others might benefit from his work.

Fig 7-2—Arch Doty, K8CFU (left) with John Lindholm, W1XX (right). Arch is remembered for his pioneering work with elevated radials for 160-meter verticals.

Fig 7-3—Bob Garrett, WA3EUL (now K3UL, at right). Although blind, Bob has managed to achieve a superb 160-Meter DXCC total of over 250 countries worked.

Shortly after 1980, Bob Garrett, WA3EUL (K3UL), begins operating 160 meters from his QTH in Williamsport, Pennsylvania. At last count, he has now achieved over 260 countries on Topband. Bob's achievement is unique, though, and deserves special mention here as he is totally blind. In spite of his handicap, he has managed to train himself to work around his blindness using mechanical devices and his hearing instead of his eyes. These enable him to tune his transmitter and linear. Enunciators play a key role here and also assist with packet spots. Bob is able to locate frequencies on the band with remarkable precision. He also climbs his tower now and then to perform simple antenna work.

Listening to Bob navigate the band with great success has become a special joy to those who know him. He is an inspiration for others who may follow, in much the same way Cliff Corne, K9EAB, was in the 1960s. In his day, Cliff achieved DXCC Honor Roll status operating from an iron lung and was a superb CW DXer. Bob Garrett, like Cliff, has achieved his share of

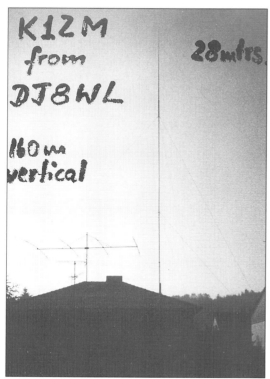

Fig 7-4—DJ8WL's 160-meter vertical, circa 1984.

success without fanfare, and if one were not aware of his special situation, it would be nearly impossible to detect it over the air.

On the DXCC front once again, the first Germans to make the 160-meter grade were Jara, DL1YD, and Peter, DJ8WL, in late 1983 at #31 and #33, respectively. Ron, GW3YDX, also known previously as G3YDX, reaches the century mark early in 1984. Stuart, GM3YCB, and Roger, G3RBP, close out the Europeans, finishing within the first 50 DXCC holders in 1984.

In this period, Pierre Petry, HB9AMO, is often heard on 160. He too achieves his DXCC, #68, early in 1985 and then goes on to achieve the first-ever 40-zone WAZ on Topband in the late 1980s. His last contact to complete this feat was with KC6MX in Zone #27 operated by Paul, K1XM.

About 1983, your author and WØZV arrive on the band and find 160 meters an enormous challenge. K1ZM receives DXCC #58 in mid-1984 and WØZV nets #90 in early 1985. Rick Roderick, K5UR, now a fixture on 160 meters with close to 280 DXCC countries, achieves a quick DXCC, #49 in April 1984. Jerry Rosalius, WB9HAD (WB9Z), begins taking an interest in Topband during this period. He continues to be quite active on the band to this day and has now achieved over 250 countries worked on 160 meters, one of the finest totals from the USA Midwest!

Long a fixture on the band following a move to Western Australia in 1969, Mike Bazley, VK6HD (ex-G3HDA), achieves a most difficult DXCC, #109, on June 11, 1985, the first Oceania station to do so. Peter Watson, ZL3GQ, finishes slightly thereafter netting DXCC #146, on March 5, 1986. Both of these fine fellows, more than a hemisphere away from any other populated continent, deserve special praise for achieving their awards. It is not easy to do this from that part of the world!

Fig 7-5—Jeff Briggs, K1ZM, in his New York shack. Jeff has confirmed over 280 countries on 160 meters.

Fig 7-6—Rick Roderick, K5UR, in his shack. Rick led the 160-Meter DXCC Honor Roll for over 10 years from his fine QTH outside Little Rock, Arkansas.

Fig 7-7—Jerry Rosalius, WB9Z, who operates from Crescent City, Illinois. Jerry's signal is one of the very best on 160 meters from the Midwest.

Fig 7-8—Mike Bazely, VK6HD, in his shack near Perth. Mike is remembered for achieving the first DXCC from Oceania, #109 overall.

It should be noted that VK6HD achieved 160-Meter DXCC *before* netting WAC. Getting into South America is no small feat on 160 meters from Perth, Australia. It took Mike another 10 years after achieving his DXCC before he finally worked the XRØY expedition for his last continent for WAC. Peter notes that his lack of darkness overlap with Eastern Europe at his sunset makes those QSOs extremely difficult for him as well.

About 1986, Peter Hutter, WW2Y, begins taking an interest in Topband. Along with friends John Fischer, N2NU, and Rob "Wackey Iraqi" Flory, K2WI, together they develop some very fine gain antennas on 160 meters and a well engineered contest station. In recent years, they have produced some excellent results in the difficult multi-operator class during the *CQ* WW and ARRL 160-Meter contests.

In fact, their efforts have spawned an exciting rivalry on Topband that takes place during *CQ* 160-Meter Contests between their team and a fine crew at station W2GD, led by John Crovelli, also a member of the Frankford Radio Club. Team W2GD and company, operating directly on the Atlantic Ocean at the USCG Station in Sandy Hook, NJ, has maximized the natural advantages of coastal propagation that exist on Topband and has produced some enormous scores over the years. Team WW2Y, to its credit, has developed some very fine transmitting and receiving antennas to compensate for an inland location at Princeton, NJ, some 75 miles away. The result has been some titanic battles in recent years in the *CQ* 160-Meter Tests and each team has enjoyed an equal measure of success. Well done, men!

Fig 7-9—Peter Hutter, WW2Y, with Riki, 4X4NJ. Both are well known on 160 meters today.

Fig 7-10—Randy Schaaf, W9ZR (left) with his son Adam, KF8XL (right). Randy has a terrific Midwest signal on Topband and holds 160-Meter DXCC #54.

The first African DXCC, #199 is finally achieved in 1987 by Bert, ZS5LB, whose fine signal can often be heard at his sunrise, especially around the equinox periods. Well done Bert—it isn't easy from your part of the world either.

From the former Soviet Union, Fred Barkov, UT5AB, operating near Kiev, makes the grade on May 1, 1985, achieving DXCC #92. Fred's achievement is followed by Karlen, UG6GAW; Vlad, UA3PFN; Valentine, UA9CBO; Vlad, UA2FF; Vlad, UB5ZAL, and club station UR1RWX in that order as we move into 1986.

Hereabouts in the USA, the Midwest stalwarts take their bows as follows: Charlie O'Brien, ex-W2EQS, having moved to the 9th district as W9NFC, finishes his DXCC and achieves #12. San Hutson, K5YY (K5QHS), of DXpedition fame, nets #18 in late 1980. Don, K8MFO, makes the grade early in 1984 achieving #42. Joe, AD8I, achieves #50 DXCC, in April 1984. Randy, W9ZR, still a major force on the band from the Midwest follows with #54 in May 1984. John Goller, K9UWA, operating from Indiana receives #61 in 1984. John, it should be noted, later achieves a superlative 40-zone Topband WAZ, a truly remarkable feat from the USA and North America. Great job, John.

Charlie Dewey, W0CD, follows soon thereafter, netting DXCC #65 from Michigan. Charlie, it should be noted, with help from friends George Taft, W8UVZ, and George Guerin, K8GG,

The first African DXCC, #199, is finally achieved in 1987 by Bert, ZS5LB. . .

later develops the famous "Battle Creek Special" antenna for use as a loaner by 160-meter DXpeditioners. This fine low-angle radiator is later used with great success at 3Y5X, VP8SGP, V51, VKØIR and many other spots. Well done, Charlie, George and George! These efforts are much appreciated by 160-meter DXers and have been responsible for many, many new ones for the deserving on Topband.

Ron Moorefield, W8ILC, and Al Hix, W8AH, round out the first Midwestern 160-Meter DXCCs achieved within the initial 100 when they receive #89 and 100 respectively early in 1985. In the Far West, a decidedly difficult spot on 160 meters due to the lack of reliable openings into Europe, W6RW and K6SE are

Fig 7-11—John Goller, K9UWA, enjoying himself at the 160-meter dinner at the Dayton HamVention in 1996.

Fig 7-12—Two of the "Battle Creek Best," Charlie Dewey, WØCD (left), and George Taft, W8UVZ (right).

followed by Ed Martinson, WØGYH; Otto Degner, W5YU; Fred Lindsey, NØXA; Jerald Slama, K7VIC; Walt Wessel, WØCM; Larry Hart, W7IUV; Brad Bradshaw, W6DAO; Gary Ernst, KØGVB; Stan Handa, W7WA; Joel Rubenstein, KA5W; Ken Fattmann, NAØY; Lloyd Rigg, W6AJJ; George Wise, W7MB; Gary Gompf, W7FG; Steve Protas, K7SP, and Mike Crabtree, ABØX. Darrell Bevan, N6DX, is often heard on the band in this period. He now sports one of the highest DXCC totals on Topband from the Far West. Congratulations are due to all, as these achievements are recognized by most savvy 160-meter ops as being *far more difficult* than the typical East Coast DXCC, which has almost become routine by this time!

On January 1, 1987, Belgium becomes one of the last countries in Europe to again open up 1.8 MHz to its amateurs. At the stroke of midnight, John Devoldere, ON4UN, fires up on the band and achieves 100 countries less than 2 months later! In 10 short years, John has managed to acquire 276 countries on Topband as of last count. It is amazing stuff, really, and the mark of a very fine 160-meter operator.

Fig 7-13—Ed Martinson, WØGYH (right), USA Far West 160-Meter DXCC #3, with G3SZA (left). Ed's outstanding DXCC efforts follow those of W6RW and K6SE from the difficult West Coast.

Fig 7-14—Gary Ernst, KØGVB, in his shack. Sadly, Gary is now a Silent Key, but is fondly remembered by the 160-meter gang.

Fig 7-15—On the top of famous N6DX Rainbow Ridge antenna farm. From left to right: K6SE; Darrell Bevan, N6DX; W6PVB; and WB6PXP.

Fig 7-16—John Devoldere, ON4UN, in his well-appointed shack near Ghent, Belgium. John achieved 160-Meter DXCC in approximately two months! He has a superb 160-meter signal.

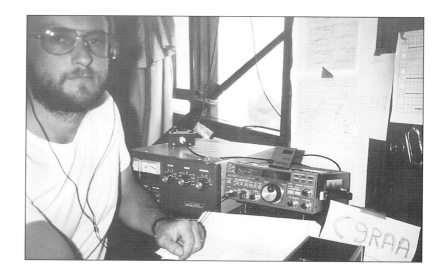

Fig 7-17—Well-known DX-peditioner Rudi Klos, DK7PE, at C9RAA. Rudi has provided many a "new one" to Topbanders.

Newcomer Rudi Klos, DK7PE, provides the 160-meter "deserving" with some real excitement beginning in the early 1980s through his many DXpeditions, including C9RAA, TNØCW, 8Q7CW and others, just to name a few. While other groups grudgingly give 160 meters a go almost as an afterthought, Rudi takes to the band with great relish whenever he is on the road. Rudi can always be counted on to know the 160-meter openings, put out a great signal from almost anywhere and be able to hear just about anything. This is no small feat and Rudi soon endeared himself to all of the 160-meter faithful. To 160-meter ops, he becomes almost a beacon and a model for other DXpeditioners to emulate when they activate a rare one. Well done, Rudi.

K1PBW retires during this period and W1HT has been off 160 meters from about 1977. W1BB observes that 160 meters now sounds like "just another fine DX band" with global DX routinely available. Stew suggests that it may be time for him to cease publication of his famous *160-Meter DX Bulletin*, but his friends persuade him to continue. Stew does so until the end of 1981, when his failing eyesight finally forces him to pass the baton over to Ivan Payne, VE3INQ (now VE3DO). Soon thereafter, W1BB is heard for the final times on Topband, and the end of an era has occurred.

Chapter 8

160-Meter DXing Chronology, 1990 To Present

160 meters has indeed developed into a superb DX band. Over 300 countries are known to be active and single-season DXCCs can now be attained even by moderately equipped DXers with perseverance. Multi-multi stations during

Fig 8-1—Some of the loudest 160-meter JAs on the USA East Coast today. From left to right: Hiro, JF1NZW; Key, JR1EBE; Ogi, JA1CGM, with K1ZM at rear under hanging sign.

the *CQ* WW DX Contest find it possible to work 85 countries during a single weekend. Well equipped single operator stations as far west as Illinois in the USA now find it possible to do the same under favorable conditions.

Sadly, in May of 1990, W1BB passes away, having spent his final years in a nursing home. The text of his obituary as it appeared in the *Boston Globe* of May 8, 1990, is shown in the sidebar. Stew is also fondly remembered by VE3DO in the *Topband Annual News Digest* of 1989/1990 and his passing is mourned by all he touched over the years. His spirit and dedication to 160 meters shall never be forgotten, however. His contribution was legendary. Stew Perry was truly an Elmer for *several generations* of 160-meter DXers who carry on in his footsteps today!

Stewart Perry, 86

Was pioneer in amateur radio

Services will be held at 11 a.m. today in the Boston Church of the New Jerusalem (Swedenborgian) on Beacon Hill for Stewart S. Perry, an amateur radio operator since the medium's early days and a retired sales engineer with the former Worthington Corp. of Cambridge, a maker of industrial power generating equipment.

Mr. Perry died Saturday in Normandy House nursing home in Melrose. He was 86 and a lifelong resident of Winthrop.

Inspired by listening to transmissions about the doomed ocean liner Titanic on a friend's short-wave radio in 1912, Mr. Perry built his first radio set that year. He was 8.

He was a teen-ager when he received his station license, W1BB, on the first day the government issued the permits. He became known by the correspondents in 100 countries as a pioneer in transmitting on the 160-meter wavelength, which was difficult to use.

Mr. Perry was allowed to put up an antenna on the water tower at Point Shirley and to string wires in Winthrop.

A graduate of Winthrop High School and the Massachusetts Institute of Technology, Mr. Perry retired from Worthington in 1966 after nearly 40 years with the firm.

He leaves his wife Marguerite (Loukes) two sons, Stewart of Yarmouthport and James N. of Fremont, Calif., and five grandchildren.

(A)

(B)

Fig 8-2—At A, Koh, JA1GTF in his shack, with his FB 160-meter vertical antenna at B.

Fig 8-3—Petr, OK1DOT, one of the most consistent 160-meter signals from Central Europe.

Fig 8-4—Bob Parkes, A45XF (VS5RP, P29PR, 4S7RPG) with Tony, A45ZZ (seated). Two fine catches on any band!

Fig 8-5—Victor, 4S7VK (left) and Bob, 4S7RPG (right) in March 1997. Operating from Victor's QTH in the country, Bob managed a number of North American QSOs on 160 meters during the 1997 season.

Fig 8-6—Rosti, OK2PGU, with son Luby. Rosti was for many years one of the best 160-meter signals from Europe.

Fig 8-7—Barney, DK8ZB, and XYL, visiting VP9.

Fig 8-9—Yuki, JA6LCJ (left), and Key, JR1EBE (right) in Tokyo.

Fig 8-8—Some well-known Asian operators. From left to right: 9M2AX, JA1CHN, JF1NZW and JR1EBE at JA1GTF QTH.

Chapter 9

Notable 160 Meter Achievements

In this review of the history of 160-meter DXing, it is appropriate that we summarize some of the most significant achievements made by Topband DXers.

FIRST 160-METER WAC HOLDERS

(1) 1953—W1BB
(2) 1957—G3PU
(3) 1961—W8GDQ

FIRST 160-METER DXCC HOLDERS

(1) Stewart S. Perry, W1BB (issued November 1, 1976)
(2) Ralph Green, W1HT (issued November 1, 1976)
(3) Wallace C. Eckles, W8LRL (issued November 2, 1976)
(4) Herb Schoenbohm, KV4FZ (issued November 3, 1976)
(5) James C. (Ernie) Hemingway, K1PBW (issued February 4, 1977)

FIRST 160-METER DXCCs BY CONTINENT

Africa—Albert Lausecker, ZS5LB
Asia—Akito Nagi, JA5DQH
Europe—David R. Wilson, G3SZA
North America—Stewart S. Perry, W1BB
Oceania—Mike E. Bazley, VK6HD
South America—Rolf Rasp, PY1RO

THE FIRST 160-METER WAS HOLDERS

(1) George F. Norton, W4EEE (issued February 12, 1937)
(2) Paul Wolfe, W5GKZ (issued December 17, 1937)
(3) J. C. Whittington, W4FNC (issued March 16, 1939)

Fig 9-1—Jim Dionne, K1MEM, in his Massachusetts shack. Jim administers the CQ *WAZ* awards program and has always had a FB 160-meter signal.

160-METER WAZ (40 ZONE) HOLDERS BY CONTINENT (1997)

Africa—None
Asia—JA1GTF, 4X4NJ
Europe—HB9AMO, LZ2DF, ON4UN, G3RBP, OH1XX,
    SM4CAN, DJ8WL, SP5INQ, G3SZA, SM5EDX, ON4ACG,
    SM4HCM, IT9ZGY, SM5BHW, SM5BFJ, SM3EVR,
    SP5EWY, G3RPB, DL1YD, SM5AQD, IV3PRK
N. America—N4JF, AB9O, W3AP, K9UWA
Oceania—None
South America—PY1BVY

160-METER DXCC HOLDERS (TO #250)

(1) W1BB	(24A) OK1ATP	(48) K4DY
(2) W1HT	(25) W6RW	(49) K5UR
(3) W8LRL	(26) KH8AC/W1	(50) AD8I
(4) KV4FZ	(27) AA1K	(51) OK2PGU
(5) K1PBW	(28) GI3OQR	(52) N4KE
(6) W4BRB	(29) K1MM	(53) W2BXA
(7) W2QD	(30) K1MEM	(54) W9ZR
(8) W2DEO	(31) DL1YD	(55) K6SE
(9) W4QCW	(32) N4SU	(56) EA3VY
(10) W4YWX	(33) DJ8WL	(57) VE1BNN
(11) K4CIA	(34) WA2SPL	(58) K1ZM
(12) W9NFC	(35) W4ZR	(59) W1RR
(13) N4JJ	(36) K4UEE	(60) W4OWJ
(14) PY1RO	(37) GW3YDX	(61) K9UWA
(15) N4EA	(38) W2TQC	(62) W2FZY
(16) G3SZA	(39) GM3YCB	(63) AA4V
(17) PAØHIP	(40) W1JZ	(64) K1NA
(18) K5YY	(41) G3RBP	(65) WØCD
(19) GD4BEG	(42) K8MFO	(66) OZ1LO
(20) N4WW	(43) VE1YX	(67) OH1XX
(21) N4SF	(44) K2DSV	(68) HB9AMO
(22) W4PZV	(45) W1OO	(69) W1JR
(23) W5SUS	(46) W3AP	(70) DL9KR
(24) G3RPB	(47) K2UU	(71) W2BHM

(72) W1WAI	(92) UT5AB	(112) K8CCV
(73) W9CG	(93) W2JB	(113) WØGYH
(74) W2FCR	(94) AA4MM	(114) G3YUV
(75) JA5DQH	(95) G3ZFC	(115) K2RIH
(76) JA2GQO	(96) W2LPE	(116) W3UM
(77) 4X4NJ	(97) K4AQQ	(117) W8JIN
(78) W4MGN	(98) N4RJ	(118) K2TQC
(79) K4PI	(99) None	(119) W3CV
(80) W2SM	(100) W8AH	(120) OZ7YY
(81) DJ8FW	(101) K5GO	(121) VE1ZZ
(82) PA3BFM	(102) W3GH	(122) F6BKI
(83) N1ACH	(103) 4Z4DX	(123) N4KG
(84) DL1RK	(104) K1ZZ	(124) DL7AA
(85) K2VV	(105) G3XTT	(125) W5YU
(86) JA1GTF	(106) K3UA	(126) W2QHH
(87) W2OKM	(107) N4NX	(127) G4AKY
(88) W5TO	(108) YU3EF	(128) W2FP
(89) W8ILC	(109) VK6HD	(129) W4FX
(90) WØZV	(110) OE5KE	(130) OZ7JZ
(91) KA1PE	(111) KG4W	(131) WB2CZB

Fig 9-2—First African 160-Meter DXCC holder, Bert, ZS5LB. Bert has always had a superb Topband signal at his sunrise. He also holds the WAZ award.

(132) K1LPS	(172) W3RCQ	(212) G3BDQ
(133) WD9AHJ	(173) UA9CBO	(213) NAØY
(134) WA8TXT	(174) UA2FF	(214) W3FM
(135) K5NA	(175) UB5ZAL	(215) W6AJJ
(136) I2BBJ	(176) K4CNW	(216) W4BAA
(137) W2LW	(177) OK3CQD	(217) SVØAA
(138) OK2BOB	(178) W2LZX	(218) K8GG
(139) NØXA	(179) HB9CIP	(219) OK1DXS
(140) K7VIC	(180) GM3WTA	(220) K8CFU
(141) N4JF	(181) CT4BD	(221) W7MB
(142) K3FN	(182) K1IU	(222) WB9NSZ
(143) OK3EY	(183) W2VO	(223) W4DHZ
(144) UG6GAW	(184) LZ2DF	(224) RT4UA
(145) W3GG	(185) TG9NX	(225) UA4HBW
(146) ZL3GQ	(186) HB9AHL	(226) KS9U
(147) T77V	(187) K9AB	(227) WB9HAD
(148) WØCM	(188) G4AAW	(228) K1XM
(149) I2ZGC	(189) SP5INQ	(229) SM7BIC
(150) F6BWO	(190) N4IN	(230) KM5H
(151) JA3ONB	(191) UR1RWX	(231) W7FG
(152) W5AQ	(192) OK1DOT	(232) W2PN
(153) W1AX	(193) OK1JDX	(233) W1AB
(154) K2CL	(194) None	(234) WA4VDE
(155) KM1H	(195) K8ZH	(235) DJ6RX
(156) K1IK	(196) W7IUV	(236) None
(157) G4OBK	(197) W6DAO	(237) K7SP
(158) LA2GV	(198) 9Y4VU	(238) ABØX
(159) GM3ZSP	(199) ZS5LB	(239) W1NG
(160) OK1DTN	(200) None	(240) FM5WD
(161) W2XN	(201) KØGVB	(241) F9YZ
(162) VE2FYR	(202) K1ST	(242) SMØAJU
(163) K2EK	(203) SM6EHY	(243) W1FZ
(164) N4WJ	(204) OK3CQR	(244) WAØIDK
(165) YU2TW	(205) OK1DWJ	(245) GM3ITN
(166) K9RJ	(206) AB9O	(246) WØPGI
(167) UA3PFN	(207) W7AWA	(247) W2GVX
(168) K9GX	(208) W9YYG	(248) KJ9I
(169) W8UVZ	(209) W4VQ	(249) JA7AO
(170) None	(210) K4TEA	(250) W4UW
(171) F8VJ	(211) KA5W	

Fig 9-3—Three of Colorado's best on Topband. From left to right: AAØRS (G3SZA), Steve "Lance Johnson" Gecewicz, KØCS and John Brosnahan, WØUN. KØCS is the editor of *The Low Band Monitor,* a must-read publication for those active on 160 meters today.

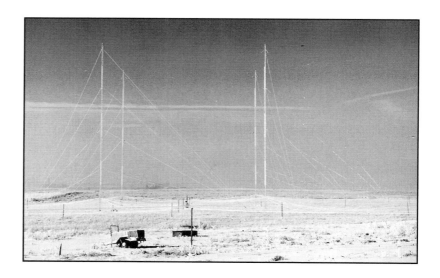

Fig 9-4—The Four Square array at AAØRS.

160-METER DXCC ACHIEVEMENT LEVELS (1996)

(As reported by K5FUV in the ARRL Annual DXCC Listing of March 1997)*

200—W4MGN, W2BHM, W3UM, SM6CVX, K1IU, NAØY, WB2P, K3UA, K4UEE, KJ9I, SM6CTQ, SP5EWY
210—K9RJ, W4OWJ, W1OO, W2JB, W3GH, K4PI, K4TEA, W1JR
220—W8UVZ, DJ6RX, W1JZ, K2CL, OZ1LO, W2BXA, W4FX
230—WØCD, SM5EDX, W2VO, N4KG
240—W2OKM, K1MEM, W2TQC
250—W9ZR, N4SU, K8MFO, DJ8WL, W1NG, W3AP, N4JJ, W8AH, WB9Z, NØXA
260—ON4UN
270—K1ZM, K5UR, W4DR
280—WØZV

* Includes only active DXCC participants in 1996 period.

Chapter 10

"Best-Ever" 160-Meter DXing Anecdotes

AS TOLD BY TOP 160-METER DXERS

Over the years, each 160-meter DXer experiences unique moments chasing Topband DX. Sometimes it is the thrill of bagging a *new one*, or maybe it's simply a "personal best" QSO that is memorable. It may be the discovery of a new quirk of Topband propagation, previously unknown to that operator. Each of these individual milestones is a precious memory that is fondly looked back upon, in some cases for many years, by the amateur involved.

Here now is a collection of these memorable moments in anecdotal form. Many of these were originally reported by the stations indicated on the 160-Meter Internet Reflector, a service provided to 160-meter DXers by Bill Fisher, W4AN (K4AAA, ex-KM9P) and are used with permission. Others were submitted directly to the author for inclusion in this chapter.

ROLF RASP, PY1RO

One of my most memorable moments on 160 meters was the time I was CQing on what I thought was a dead band. 4S7GV

Fig 10-1—Rolf Rasp, PY1RO, and Bill McDowell, K4CIA.

came back to me with an S7 signal. He was using a single 807 with 20 W out and had never worked any real DX until then.

Another was the making of the first PY/Australia QSO on June 5, 1987, with VK7BC. It was a huge thrill as it was not a sked. But VK7 was still not a QSO on the Australian mainland, which is what I made on August 5, 1990, with VK4YB. This was not a sked either! Roger had spent a month with us in Rio a number of years before when he was touring in his Land Rover with his now-XYL Mary.

Hearing my first 160-meter signals ever was also a special moment as an SWL: PY1-9247 on February 5, 1962. I copied WØGBV in QSO with K8BBI. My receiver at the time was a modified converter into a broadcast receiver with absolutely no filters. Why did I modify that converter to try to listen to 160 meters? I was repeatedly reading W1BB's comments in *QST*'s DX column and had written to Stew. He gave me all the help he could to get me started. I met Stew personally first on Easter weekend 1964 and a number of times afterward, as my work took me frequently to the Boston area. Those eyeball QSOs with "Mr 160" and those sessions at *the tower* will be fond memories forever!

Fig 10-2—Aki, JA5DQH (AH0C), and XYL Rie, AH0D, at their wedding in 1992.

AKITO NAGI, JA5DQH

I have made a lot of memorable QSOs on 160 meters, but I consider those with my last three continents in late 1974 to be my most unforgettable ones. These were with DL1FF (EU), PY1RO (SA) and ST2AY (AF). One should remember that in 1975 when I achieved my 160-Meter WAC, no one in Japan even considered it a possibility to complete a 160-Meter DXCC from JA. But when the band was opened in the USSR for the first time in 1979, this created new opportunities for JA DXers as many new countries became available that were relatively close to JA. The availability of more commercial gear also opened the band more readily to all hams worldwide—160 meters was no longer just for the maniacal few!

At the time many JA stations and I would get up at 0300 hours local time and attempt to work into the USSR in order to boost our DXCC totals. I myself had the honor of making the first-ever JA QSOs with 9 of the 18 available USSR republics. This for me was also a major thrill as it helped me become the first JA to achieve a DXCC on 160 meters, #75 in 1984.

I should like to add a bit more. One cannot talk about 160 meters without mentioning Stew, W1BB. Tracing his story alone tells much of the history of Topband. I had dozens of skeds with him but could never make a QSO. But this experience and challenge led me to a new eagerness for 160 meters. Also, we should not forget the very fine activity of JA3AA, JA7AO, 4X4NJ, VS6DO and 9M2AX in Asia, where activity in general is very low.

FERNANDO FERNANDEZ MARTIN, EA8AK

Probably my most memorable QSO was the one I made with KH6XX. For more than two years at my sunrise I had skedded Randy Sobol without any success. Then surprisingly, without any previous sked I made a wonderful QSO on CW, which was

Fig 10-3—Fernando, EA8AK, in his shack on Tenerife. Always a big signal, Fernando has 35 zones confirmed on 160 meters and considers a QSO with KH6XX one of his best.

followed a couple of minutes later on SSB. Another memorable QSO was with Jim Smith via long path when he was signing P29JS in Papua New Guinea.

From here, probably my toughest area to work into on 160 meters is Southeast Asia. I still have not worked zones 26 and 27. Today you find more activity out of these zones but I am no longer as active as I once was. I have 35 zones confirmed and still need 12, 22, 23, 26 and 27.

About Stew Perry, W1BB, well what can I say? What a great season! What a great season!

BERT LAUSECKER, ZS5LB

My best long-distance QSO on 160 meters was with KH6 but from South Africa the toughest countries to work are in Zones 1 and 2. Other toughies include ZL, DU and HS. Of these, I have managed to work KL7 and ZL. So far I have 35 zones confirmed and I am finding Zones 26 and 40 especially difficult also.

I started listening on this band 30 years ago using homebrew converters. During all my years of operating I always liked 80 and 160 meters. After completing 5BDXCC, 5BWAS and 5BWAZ, I have spent more time on this exciting band!

DENNIS SHAPIRO, W1UF

My most memorable moment on 160 meters occurred on June 11, 1977. After being licensed for 30 years, I finally put up an antenna that would work on Topband and I was QRV. It was 2125 Z, which was 5:25 PM local time, and there were no stations to be heard. I called CQ and back came W1BB/1.

We exchanged reports, etc. Stew said he was at his summer QTH in Harrington, Maine. I told him that this was my very first 160-meter QSO. He came back with congratulations and commented that this was special and needed something special in commemoration. During the QSO, we discovered that we were both MIT graduates. We signed and I felt exhilarated at the warm welcome from *Mr Topband* himself.

A few days later, I received in the mail a hunk of birch bark, roughly 6.5 by 3.5 inches. It was written in longhand on both sides:

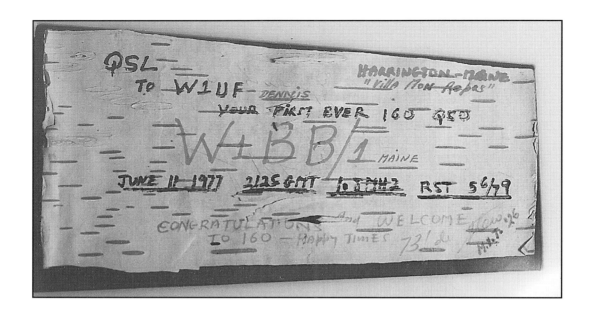

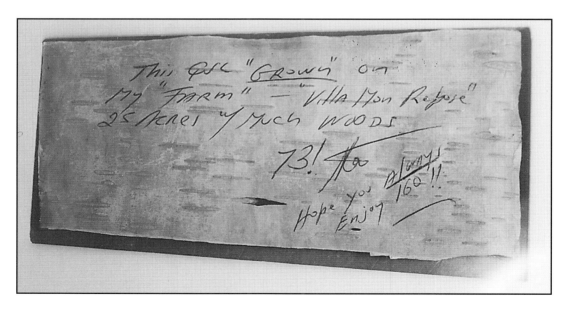

Fig 10-4—W1BB/1 fanciful QSL to W1UF, confirming Dennis' first 160-meter QSO on June 11, 1977. This was made out of birchbark wood and was lettered by hand!

Harrington, Maine
Villa Mon Repose
QSL to W1UF — Dennis
Your first-ever 160 QSO
W1BB/1 Maine
June 11, 1977 2125 GMT 1.8 MHz RST 5 6/7 9
Congratulations and Welcome
  to 160 — Happy Times
73 de Stew, MIT '26

The reverse side said:

This QSL Grown on my Farm
Villa Mon Repose
25 Acres of much woods
73! Stew
Hope you Always Enjoy 160!

I've had this mounted between two pieces of plastic, 6×9 inches, with a spacer in between so as to protect the bark. It is one of my proudest possessions!

JOHN DEVOLDERE, ON4UN

Although it is difficult to choose, my best QSOs ever on 160 meters would have to include FOØCI, FK8CP, FT5ZR, 3YØPI and all contacts made with Jack, KH6CC. Also, my QSO with JTØXC in Zone 23, which was my 40th zone on 160 meters, stands out in my mind.

From here in Western Europe, the Central Pacific is probably the toughest area of the world to work into on 160, principally because of the distance and because much of it is over the pole from here. KL7 is also very difficult because of the aurora. I have only worked KL7Y in 1987 and last winter. It is rarely done except at a sunspot minimum from here.

MIKE BAZLEY, VK6HD

The hardest part of the world to work into from here is South America, as we have to go over the South Pole and this attenuates signals. Therefore, working XRØY to finish off my 160-meter WAC was very satisfying for me. I got my DXCC in 1985 but had to wait another 10 years for the WAC to be completed—HI. I have only heard four other South American stations from out here since 1970. One of these was Rolf, PY1RO. I heard him but, unfortunately, he did not hear my signals.

It must be recorded that without the encouragement of W1BB I am sure I would have given this band away. Stew used to send out his *Bulletin* and always had some supportive remarks to go with it. There is no doubt in my mind that this gentleman deserves the highest praise and we should ensure that his pioneering work is not forgotten.

JOHN GOLLER, K9UWA

One of my most memorable moments occurred on November 8, 1985. I was up early tuning around to see if I could hear any DX or JAs. I heard a couple of weak ones so I knew the band was open. I kept looking for something new and checked the JA window on the second VFO. All of a sudden I heard KH6CC about 1905 kHz, just outside the JA window. I decided to listen, wondering what is Jack doing up here anyway? This is not

Fig 10-5—K9UWA in his shack. Note the Geochron clock prominently mounted on the wall to really highlight the times for gray line QSOs.

where he usually belongs as normally he hangs out around 1830/32 kHz.

Oh, he is calling JA0APE. No, wait a minute, he is calling JT0APE! So, obviously, I began to listen very, very closely. *Yes, Yes, Yes*—I can actually hear the JT! So, up goes the keyer speed to 35 WPM and I tail-end the JT, saying JACK PSE DE K9UWA.

Jack goes back and finishes his QSO/report and I am *dying*! Waiting... waiting... *Bingo*! Jack says QRX for the K9 on freq! I send! JT0APE DE K9UWA UR 339 339 339 BT and JT0APE comes back RRR UR 339 339 339. I go back RRR, PSE QRL W8 ON FREQ. I think it was W8JI if I remember correctly that had found us and dumped his call in as the JT was turning it back to me. I think he may have worked him too and *bam*, the band slammed shut for me. My QSO was 1215 Z, just about my sunrise! After I peeled myself off the ceiling and quit shaking I thought *wow*! Damn glad I still had the Drakes and homebrew amp as the SWR was really lousy at 1905 kHz!

My next most memorable one, and again, I was really, really *lucky*, was when Gopal, VU2GDG, went to the Andamans. I needed it for an all-time DXCC new one and hoped against all odds for a QSO. Obviously I wanted him badly on 160. Well, I worked him easily on 40, so I got the all-time new one for DXCC but there was not a real charge in that one.

Then I was getting ready for the *CQ* WW SSB test October 22, 1987, and *Bingo*, I hear a guy calling VU4GDG on 1840 kHz SSB. It sounded like the caller knew he was there but couldn't quite hear Gopal. So I asked "Well, how about I give him a call?? de K9UWA." Somebody said give him a try.

So I go "VU4GDG VU4GDG from K9UWA. You're 3/3 over." He comes back and says "Roger Roger Roger, K9UWA. You're 3/3 3/3. Thanks." That was at 0005 Z on October 23, 1987. This became a *turning point* for me because it was at this moment that I realized I might one day achieve a 40-zone WAZ on 160 meters. My only tough one left was Zone 24 and I figured I would eventually snag VS6DO. That would leave a couple of difficult African zones from the "Black Hole" but it would be just a matter of time until someone put on a real DXpedition to what I still needed! By the way, I define a *real* DXpedition as being a concerted effort on 160 meters and working *me*!

RIKI KLINE, 4X4NJ

Some of my most memorable times on 160 meters occurred in 1973 while operating the ARRL 160 Contest. I had been encouraged to get on the band by Stew, W1BB, who had been sending me his newsletters for several years. It happened that year that Martin, VE3MR, was visiting Israel and told me there was strong interest among Topbanders about getting 4X on 160. He invited me to operate from his 4X4 QTH if I could get permission to operate in a contest. After several discussions with the Ministry of Communications officials, they agreed that on a limited and trial basis, I could operate in the 1973 ARRL 160 Contest. So I was off to Martin's QTH in Netanya.

He had a top-story apartment in the Four Seasons Hotel, which was a 10-story structure practically sitting on the Mediterranean. I strung a full-sized sloping dipole from the roof of the hotel to a ground stake on the beach right at the edge of the sea.

The contest started and I worked quite a few Europeans and then worked Stew, W1BB, for the first-ever W/4X QSO! Stew was as ecstatic as I was about the QSO and his QSL is decorated with colored marker superlatives. After about two hours into the contest, I also worked Rolf, PY1RO. Then Murphy got to me as the high voltage transformer in the Swan transceiver that Martin had loaned me went up in smoke. So that was the end of my first activity on 160 but it was enough to get me extremely interested in Topband!

This occasional activity, only in a few contests with a special permit, continued for over 10 years. Then, in 1984, I was invited by the Israel Amateur Radio Club to join a special committee that was serving as a consultant to the Ministry of Communications in defining Amateur Radio privileges in the new WARC bands. Now was my chance to settle the Topband issue!!

The final result was that 4X4s were given permanent privileges from 1810 to 2000 kHz and in the 1810 to 1850 segment, I was able to convince them that we should be able to use the same power that amateurs use in the USA—1500 W— which was approved. The official announcement was dated March 26, 1985, and now I was finally on my way on 160 meters.

Another of my most exciting moments on 160 meters occurred

on January 3, 1987, and it was a QSO that I never expected to make. I worked KL7Y and if you look at a globe you can see that the 4X path to KL7 goes right through the North Pole. There could not be a more difficult path for a Topband QSO from here.

Due the difficulty of making a Zone 1 QSO from here, I never expected to finish Topband WAZ, thinking that it would always be lacking. I guess that I need not explain what this meant in terms of typical absorption, etc.

Another never-to-be forgotten QSO was with the recent XRØY operation. This is because of the distance as they are almost at the antipode from here and therefore, this QSO is the longest distance I have ever worked on 160 meters. However, the path is generally east-west, and therefore, not problematical from an absorption standpoint. Signal levels were superb (599+!).

The West Coast of North America is the toughest area to work into from here—by far. Evidence of this fact is that it has taken me until early 1997 to garner my last few states, such as Nevada, Idaho and Oregon in order to finally complete my WAS award. This took many years of skeds patiently waiting for an opening!

DAVID WILSON, G3SZA/AAØRS

My most memorable moments on 160 meters would have to include my first QSO with Stew, W1BB. Stew was an inspiration; his patience was immense; he would never give up on a call, especially during his "first-timer" tests. I had 10 W to a 30-foot vertical with no radials and I spent months trying to make that first DX QSO with him. It was during that time that I got hooked on 160. It was so hard, so noisy, so few stations were on...and the only thing that was stable was W1BB, who was always there.

So many newcomers to 160 meters take for granted the incredible level of activity they can enjoy these days. I even read a comment advocating the increased use of QRP. Brother, I lived with enforced QRP for years. It is awful—all it does is decrease activity, albeit over a long period of time. People in high QRN areas are not going to hurt their ears night after night just to make 5 to 10 QSOs a year. The reason there is so much DX on 160 these days is because people can hear DX even though they may not have a super station setup.

Fig 10-6—G3SZA with Dan, KL7Y. Dan has given many 160-meter DXers their Alaska QSO for WAS.

Over the past 25 years I have had the pleasure of meeting many of the early 160 DXing pioneers—W6RW, K6SE—both of these great guys opened the West Coast to Europe. K1PBW, Ernie, who reintroduced the Beverage. W9UCW, who kept the Midwest alive. I could mention countless others. But, no one comes close to the achievements of Stew Perry...he infected all of us with the 160 bug!

DON FIELD, G3XTT

My experience on 160 meters goes back only to about 1968 and even after all this time, it is easy to remember what DX was on the bands—there was relatively little of it. With limited space for aerials, and low power, it took me some time to make my first North American QSO. In the end, VO1FB went into the log. In the USA, W1HGT (now W1HT) and K1PBW were the first and only QSOs I made for a long time, until I finally put W1BB in the log.

I seem to remember that W8LRL was my next big breakthrough on the band. Although I never met W1BB, I did walk past his QTH in the summer of 1972 when I was on a working vacation in the US during my college days. I also saw his famous W1BB/1 QTH, a water tower right on the Winthrop seafront, on which he affixed an inverted-V antenna. I still have photographs of both of those locations. Incidentally, Stew's home QTH included beams for HF, so he was not exclusively a Topband operator.

DOUG ALLEN, W2CRS/Ø

One of my best moments on 160 meters was working W1BB. I first worked him as a teenager about 1960 with the call W3IFA from Maryland, but I had followed his efforts in *QST* and listened to him on my SX-99 beginning in 1956.

To this day, I have a "Compliments of W1BB—Always Be Careful" card on my bulletin board. It's the same size as a QSL card and lists seven rules such as "Never wear 'phones while working on the transmitter." The card is dated July 23, 1969.

I also remember fondly taking part in Stew's 160-Meter tests as an SWL listening with my quarter wave of wire around the yard that I used with the Viking II and SX-99 through a knife switch! I also remember chatting in the late 1960s with Ernie, K1PBW. He was quite a philosopher.

BILL TIPPETT, W4ZV

Here's a 160-meter tale from my best DXing days when I was in Colorado at my WØZV QTH. It was fall of 1991 when I heard that JJ1VKL/4S7 was going to be QRV on Topband. I didn't pay much attention to it since I figured the path was just about impossible at my location. The bearing for 4S7 is 355 degrees and Magnetic North is 13 degrees from Colorado, which I thought precluded a short path QSO. Since I had only made one long-path QSO in 7 years of operating (UA9UCO in Zone 18 before my sunrise in 1987), I figured the chances of a contact with Zone 22 were slim and none.

Nevertheless, Mit was very active on 40 and 80 long path before my sunrise with a good signal. In November, I asked him what his operating habits were on 160 and he told me he was usually around 1824 kHz after sunset on weekends. I told him I would look for him there around 1330 Z on Saturday mornings my time.

Like most successful 160 DXers, I know that patience and persistence are sometimes rewarded. I started a vigil of calling CQ DX on 1824 every Saturday morning at 1330 Z. I listened on my long-path Beverage at 210° (years of experience have proven it to be the best direction for long path on 40 and 80). November gave way to December and I kept trying. Sometime in this period I heard that Mit had worked W2GD and VE1ZZ at East Coast sunset, which is before Mit's sunrise. Others like VK6HD told me that he had a very good signal so I kept the faith that I might get lucky for that once in a million chance that we might QSO by long path.

As I remember, the morning of December 28, 1991, was very cold and I was very tempted to stay in bed. Since it was near Winter Solstice, we don't get much daylight at that time of year and my local sunrise was about 1420 Z (0720 local time). I got out of bed around 1300 Z, perked my usual pot of coffee and went down to check the band. Not much was doing as usual but I was ready to go at 1330. As the clock hit 1330, my programmable keyer started the ritual CQ DX at about 18 WPM. I learned a long time ago not to send DX calls on sked because you tend to attract a lot of the "deaf and dumb" on 160 by doing that. The keyer completed its job after about a minute and I started listening. Thank God the electric fences were quiet that day.

What is that? Someone is answering. I switch through the Beverages to see if it's someone off to the East that thinks they are DX. (I guess Colorado *is* DX to some but I'm looking for bigger game this morning.) No, the signal is definitely on the 210 degree Beverage and not on others toward VK and JA. Gosh, he's weak! I can't quite make out the call yet but someone's definitely in there answering me. QRZ QRZ QRZ DE W0ZV W0ZV K. I frantically fiddle with my faithful TS-930 and try lowering the pitch to improve the signal to noise (it works for me). Gosh! It *is* Mit as I hear W0ZV DE JJ1VKL/4S7 K!

My heart is pounding and hands are trembling as I answer, give him a 449 and write the entry in the log at 1334 Z. Mit responds and gives me a 569 and his signal is gradually building. His local sunset is about 1233 Z so maybe the band is peaking halfway between his sunset and my sunrise. RR QSL MIT 73 DE W0ZV

TU. Wow!! Charlie, KYØA, immediately calls as I am posting the QSO on the local PacketCluster. Some locals don't think 160 is a legitimate DX band... wonder what they'll think of this spot? Mit's signal is now to the point that I can get a weak recording of him working Charlie. Too bad I didn't have the presence of mind to do that for my QSO. He's very weak but just think about how FAR that signal has traveled.

Later I get a couple of pictures from Mit. He was using the "Aki Special" (made famous by JA5DQH) which is a spindly vertical about 15 meters high with a toploading wire pulled back toward the ground. It looks more like an inverted-J in the photograph, since the top part of it is a fiberglass fishing pole. I think Mit was running about 400 W output and he was receiving only with the transmit antenna—no Beverages.

This was truly the most exciting contact of my 39 years of DXing and contesting. Not just to work 4S7 from Colorado on 160, but to do it the *hard* way! Later I would actually work Mit again via skewed short path over JA, with 599 signals both ways around Spring Equinox. I have that one on tape too, but it was not as thrilling as this one. This contact and the 9V1XQ long-path QSO from here in North Carolina are what keep me coming back for more on Topband.

ED HUGHES, KG4W

I'd like to relate a QSO on 160 meters that is the one that immediately comes to mind whenever I ponder this question. Actually, there have got to be others more appropriate for my #1 but this is the one I always think of and this was on a "semi-list" to boot.

It was December 31, 1985, and I am not sure how many of my present 233 countries I had at that time but it had to be small. The Zulu time was 0125 and I was twisting the knob on CW and just listening around. As the VFO got up around the 1838-1840 area, I heard a lot of SSB goings-on. Quickly flipping to LSB, I determined that there was a European station MCing for some (hopefully rare) DX. I had no idea who the DX was, but one thing for sure, by the USA call signs I copied in the pileup, *I knew I needed it!*

The MC was taking 2-3 call signs at a time and I threw mine

in, still never having heard the DX. Lucky for me the MC got another call ahead of me, as I would have hated to have had to ask "What's his call?" So I am tweaking and peaking and getting ready and the other OM is now calling and saying "VU2GDG, last heard..." Wow, my heart pumped louder and the palms dampened and I then made my call and exchanged 55 reports with Gopal. Shortly thereafter, the activity ended and I have never heard VU again on 160 meters.

JERRY ROSALIUS, WB9Z

I have two stories to relate, both difficult paths and zones. On January 28, 1993, at 1305 Z I worked VU2/DJ9RB on 80 CW long path. He is *really* 579 on the southwest Beverage. I asked him to try 160 and he says "See you in 2 minutes." We exchange 449

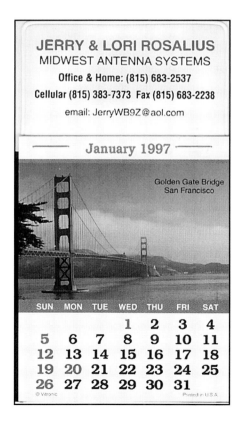

Fig 10-7—Need an antenna put up by a professional? When not working DX on 160 meters, Jerry, WB9Z, is your man!

reports at 1308 Z, which was my exact sunrise time to the minute. And, I believe it was about 20 minutes after his sunset.

My second story occurred on October 25, 1987, when I was part of the infamous VU4GDG to USA opening during the *CQ WW SSB* contest. I was operating single-band 160 meters in that contest and since the sun was just about up I was ready to call it a night. On the last check of the band I found VK9NS calling VU4GDG. I listened and I could *actually hear* Gopal! I darn near fell out of the chair. By now, the sun was on the horizon. I sat and listened to Bill, W0ZV, work him and then I started calling like never before. Tom, N4KG, beat me out first but I got his attention on the next call. But, he was having trouble with my old call WB9HAD.

Finally, after several tries he got it okay at 1205 Z. That was the last I heard of him as he was quickly in the noise and the sun was now far above the horizon. I believe it was about 30 minutes after his sunset. That has been my only Zone 26 QSO. The conditions were FB that weekend as I worked 157 DX QSOs, 23 zones and 54 countries, which at the time was a USA contest record.

MIKE GREENWAY, K4PI

I don't think any DXer can resist telling about his most

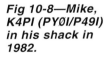
Fig 10-8—Mike, K4PI (PY0I/P49I) in his shack in 1982.

exciting QSOs. For 160, mine was in the mid-1980s, when I had been on the band for only a few years. One winter afternoon just after dark, the European beacons were nearly blowing the lid off the receiver. I did not normally call CQ but I was hearing nothing of significance so I thought why not call CQ as there might be something out there. I had never heard the beacons so strong.

I called one CQ and I heard a reply about 569. All I copied was 3AX and I thought it was probably GW3AX so I went QRZ. Then, clear as day, I heard the station sign 9M2AX at 579! We exchanged reports and names in the clear. I heard only one station call him after I was through, some VP2V... Later that night, VU2 was on SSB but a farmer's electric fence was doing 20 dB over S9. I have never heard 9M2AX again in 10 years or a VU either. Those great waves come only once or twice in a *lifetime*! Savor the moments!"

BOB WENDLING, NW6N

I had only been operating on 160 meters for a few weeks with the first antenna I had put up, which was a flop. So I decided to try about 80 feet of irrigation tubing for a vertical using bailing wire for a tophat. Man, that new antenna played. Tuning the band I hear a weak but Q5 signal calling CQ DE VP8SGP. One call and I was in the log!

After that experience, the bug bit hard and I've been stringing Beverages and building taller verticals ever since. Working VQ9TP at sunrise was a real thrill a couple of winters ago, as well as the *awesome* opening the West Coast had in December 1995 into Europe.

160 meters isn't an easy band to operate. It is not for the "shack-on-a-belt" types. And, you don't get big signals out of a box either. If you want it, you gotta *work* for it! Is it worth it? You bet!

JOHN JONES, NO0Y

I operate from a CC&R "no-outside-antenna" QTH, so every 160-meter DX QSO is a challenge. I use a $^1/_4$-wave balloon supported vertical for an antenna. Probably my most thrilling 160-meter DX was when I worked AH1A on January 30, 1993. I

Fig 10-9—Jim, K1MEM, with Jeff, K1ZM, enjoying the 160-meter suite at Dayton, mid 1980s.

had operated the CQ 160 Meter Contest all night. As dawn approached I was tuning between 1820 and 1830 kHz and heard AH1A call CQ. It was light enough outside so that I could see my balloon antenna and it was only 20 feet up. Most of the antenna wire was drifting just above the ground. Rats! It had developed a leak.

I debated going outside to pull it down and refill it. AH1A signed—no one replied. It was going to have to be now or never. I gave a quick 1×2 call using 100 W and that poor "dummy load" antenna across half a continent and thousands of miles of ocean.

Then I hear NOØY DE AH1A 599. I couldn't believe they heard me. I managed to send my exchange and confirmations. A minute later, AH1A faded into the noise and was gone. Had I gone outside to refill the balloon, I would have missed them.

BOB KILE, KG7D

It is hard to say what was or is the best contact I've had on 160 meters. Perhaps it was ZD8ANT, who called CQ for hours with no response and then answered my first call. I came back an hour later and he was still calling CQ so I called again and worked him this time for a nice 15 minute chat. I guess this was an example of "searchlight-effect propagation" on 160 meters where a DX station illuminates only a specific region of the country for a period of time—and no other.

Or, maybe it was the early-morning JA run I had in the *CQ 160 Meter Contest* several years back when I called CQ and specified the QSX frequency in kana-code to have JA7AO come back and say GOOD MORNING BOB YOU ARE 599JA!

BOB CUTTER, KIØG

What are my best 160-meter DX stories? Well, here they are short and sweet! I am at 87 countries confirmed using 5-W output power. Those are 87 pairs of the *finest ears* in hamdom and I could not single out even one as the best of the lot!

JIM DIONNE, K1MEM

My most exciting contacts on 160 meters were the first I made. G3RTY was my first European. 100 W was the limit here and I pushed it by running a Drake C-Line. Before the power limit was upped (around 1981, I think) I had worked 73 countries. Almost all of this was split-frequency work, listening above 1825 kHz and transmitting around 1805 kHz.

It often required calling for 2 hours to work a new Eastern European. If I had to pick out my best QSOs from that period, I guess VK6HD in the AM would be it and FRØFLO (FR5DX) on SSB stand out. And, I was delighted when I received Herik's QSL confirming that SSB QSO!

TOM RAUCH, W8JI

My best DX on 160 was Ern, G3PU, in the early 1960s. That was when Europeans really ran 10 W or less and people here *really* ran 100 W or less. I worked him with my homebrew single 6146 PA, homebrew 15-tube receiver and a dipole up 20 feet from Ohio.

My second best DX was DL1FF after about six months of desperate week after week effort. My very first DX contact was the most thrilling—the excitement has gone steadily downhill since. My excitement over later JTØ and 4S7 contacts is almost nil in comparison to those first contacts with Ern and Armin!

PETE RIMMEL, N8PR

My best 160-meter DX is a story of "Miles Per Watt" output. About 10 years ago, I was all ready to enter one of the major DX contests. Just before the start of the test, I was tuning up and my Henry amplifier quit. I later found out that the solder on one of the 3-500Zs had melted due to recent high-power RTTY activity. At any rate, I decided to try the contest QRP at the time. I had a 60-foot tower with a modified half sloper to the northwest. To the northeast and south were 80-meter slopers, each about 66 feet long. On top of the tower was a KT34-XA and a two-element 40-meter Yagi. The resonant frequency of the system was about 2.3 MHz.

Extending the NW sloper parallel to the ground by adding another 50 feet of wire about 10 feet above the ground (thus making the entire driven element approximately 110 feet long), I was able to get the thing to resonate well without a tuner lower in the band. Who would have guessed that this antenna would put out as good a signal as it did? I was able to work the Caribbean and a few Europeans with my QRP signal. But, imagine my surprise at my sunrise when I worked KH6CC with 5 W. It is 4800 miles to KH6 from my Florida QTH. That's about 1000 miles per watt. I happily sent for that QSL after the contest!

JEFF BRIGGS, K1ZM

Like other operators, it is hard to zero in on my best 160-meter DX moments because there have been so many over the years. Certainly, making the first-ever Caribbean to JA QSOs from NP4A was memorable. Then there was the first time I worked Japan from NY, when I worked Kinji, JA2GQO, on sked in January 1984. Or perhaps it was when I worked ZC4IO for my first Asian contact and a WAC on 160 meters from W1ZM in Connecticut in 1977. Or maybe it was sitting alongside Joe Krone, WA2SPL, at W2PV in 1975 and hearing Roger, ST2AY, from Sudan at a solid 579 for two hours on Jim's CX7A and 180-foot high inverted-V dipole!

Actually, though, I think my two most memorable moments on 160 meters would have to be when I worked XZ1N in November 1996 and when I followed this up in December 1996 with the first-ever JA long-path QSOs ever made from the East Coast of the USA on 160 meters.

Let's begin with the XZ1N story, which occurred on November 20, 1996. This expedition by some well-known and savvy operators had been eagerly anticipated by many 160-meter DXers. However, as an East Coast 160-meter DXer, I really didn't think I had any chance of working these boys on Topband. Short path is directly over the pole and the long path seemed totally out of the question. After all, I had only worked a handful of long-path DX on 160 meters in 15 years including VK6HD, 9M2AX and VK9XY.

Nevertheless, once the expedition got started, I did check the band nightly at my sunset to see what I might hear. For the first few days I did hear the European pileups calling XZ1N split above 1830 kHz and, supposedly, XZ1N was transmitting on 1825.5 kHz. However, each time I checked the XZ frequency, I couldn't detect even the presence of a signal. So, I figured at the time, "Sure—that's close. Here we go again with another Mega-DXpedition that I will get to listen to Europe and maybe VE1ZZ work!"

Somehow, though, the night of November 20, 1996, was different. The band sounded extra solid and the Europeans were very, very loud as it grew dark at my QTH. I knew from Internet

Fig 10-10—The author, K1ZM, at W1ZM, about 1979.

Fig 10-11—XZ1N QSL to K1ZM, for 160-meter long-path QSO on November 21, 1996. (The QSL shows a signal strength of 599 "Contest Style" but was not the actual 559 RST sent!)

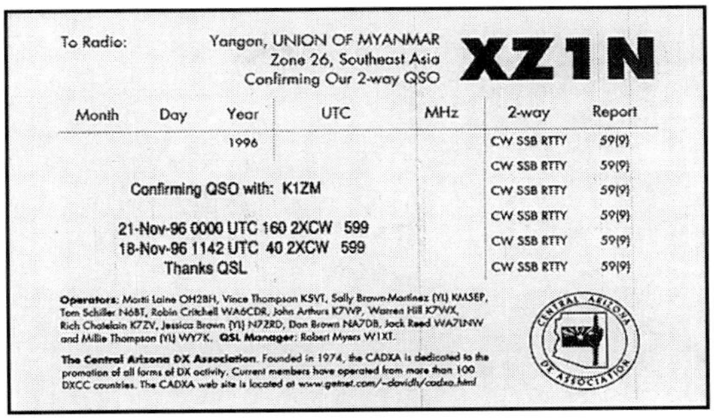

To Radio: Yangon, UNION OF MYANMAR
Zone 26, Southeast Asia
Confirming Our 2-way QSO

XZ1N

Month	Day	Year	UTC	MHz	2-way	Report
		1996			CW SSB RTTY	59(9)
					CW SSB RTTY	59(9)
Confirming QSO with: K1ZM					CW SSB RTTY	59(9)
					CW SSB RTTY	59(9)
21-Nov-96 0000 UTC 160 2XCW 599					CW SSB RTTY	59(9)
18-Nov-96 1142 UTC 40 2XCW 599					CW SSB RTTY	59(9)
Thanks QSL						

Operators: Martti Laine OH2BH, Vince Thompson K5VT, Sally Brown-Martinez (YL) KM5EP, Tom Schiller N6BT, Robin Critchell WA6CDR, John Arthurs K7WP, Warren Hill K7WX, Rich Chatelain K7ZV, Jessica Brown (YL) N7ZRD, Don Brown NA7DB, Jack Reed WA7LNW and Millie Thompson (YL) WY7K. QSL Manager: Robert Myers W1XT.

The Central Arizona DX Association, Founded in 1974, the CADXA is dedicated to the promotion of all forms of DX activity. Current members have operated from more than 100 DXCC countries. The CADXA web site is located at www.getnet.com/~davidh/cadxa.html

that XZ1N was there on 1825.5 so I kept switching between the European pileup calling him and his transmit frequency. Hearing nothing on 1825.5, I only had the exciter turned on and I was actually reading the daily paper at the time. At about 2335 Z, I thought I heard a signal transmitting in synch with the calling going on above 1830 kHz. I listened hard and, lo and behold, *yes*, it was XZ1N and his signal was building up!

On goes the amplifier. By now, I am beginning to get really excited because this is not only a possible new country for me but it is also in Zone 26, which I have never worked on 160 meters. I start calling and it seems hopeless at first but after about 10 minutes, a European advises XZ1N that North America is hearing and calling him. By now, W3BGN and W8LRL have joined the pack with me and I figured they both were also hearing the XZ as they were calling in proper sequence.

The next 15 minutes seemed an eternity because, even though the XZ1N asked for North America *only* on 1828 kHz, the Europeans *never* stopped calling. Some even elected to transmit nearly non-stop on 1825.5 kHz, which made it impossible to hear what XZ1N was doing. Several times I thought he may have answered me but I really wasn't sure, so I just kept dumping my call in. Soon it was 2355 Z, the XZ was dropping from a peak of 559 to a very watery 449 as he went into daylight and I thought it was all over with for the evening.

Then, for one brief moment, the European chatter subsided on 1825.5 kHz and I heard K1ZM K1ZM K1ZM 559 559 559 K. I was so blitzed it was all I could do to reply RRR UR 449 449 449 449 DE K1ZM K1ZM K1ZM BK.

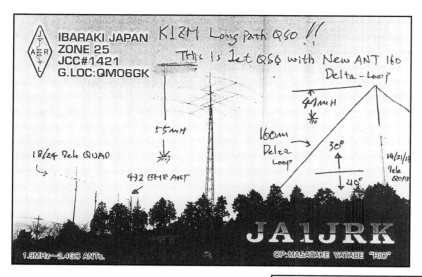

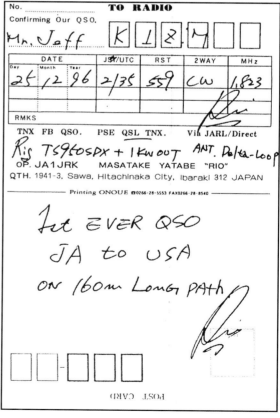

Fig 10-12—QSL card from JA1JRK to
K1ZM, confirming first 160-meter
East Coast long-path QSO to Japan
on December 25, 1996, a lovely Merry
Christmas present for both amateurs!

Then the XZ operator totally floored me by sending R CFM CFM CFM K1 K1 K1 BK, which I did not initially understand. So I again reply with DE K1ZM K1ZM K1ZM UR 449 449 449 BK. XZ1N then sends another "CFM" and he goes into the log at 2359 to 0001 Z on 20/21 November 1996. I was, by now, a total basket case. I called W4ZV to tell him the story, but Bill was out and I headed instead to get a cool frosty from the 'fridge. It was pretty darned exciting making a QSO on 160 meters that I never thought possible—and doing it the *hard* way by long path.

My other special moment on 160 meters occurred about a month later when I was operating from my new home on Cape Cod, Massachusetts. This spot is on an island and will become my future retirement home before too long. It was specifically selected for low-band DX work and offers significant advantages on the long path into Asia on 160 meters. Sunset is earlier than

Fig 10-13—*K1ZM's long-path view toward JA1JRK from his QTH on Cape Cod, Massachusetts. [Doesn't that make you drool?—Ed.]*

any spot in the continental USA, except for the northeast tip of Maine where it meets VE1/New Brunswick. I hoped I would now be able to work some of the neat LP Asia stuff VE1ZZ is always working from Nova Scotia. I especially wanted to see if I could hear and work into JA by long path on Topband. Jack had done it in late 1995 and again in early 1996, but no USA East Coast amateur had managed a QSO yet.

I started listening at sunset on December 20 around 2100 Z and continued listening daily in the JA "window" for the next four days. Hearing nothing at all, I almost did not bother to go into the shack on Christmas day but decided to anyway at 2130 Z as it grew dark outside. As soon as I tuned across 1910 kHz, I was startled by a huge JA pileup calling 1AØKM. There must have been 20 JA signals audible from the sound of it, with JA1JRK a solid 579 and JA1HQT about 3 dB down from Rio's signal!

What to do? What to do? I had heard JA long path from NY in late 1995 but the opening is very short and it is very difficult to attract the JA's attention when you hear them from the East Coast. I listened for 30 seconds and no JA was calling CQ listening QSX down, so I first thought I would miss this golden opportunity. So, I spotted *myself* on packet hoping that my spot would be picked up on the OH2BUA cluster and maybe seen in time by one of the JAs I was hearing on their cluster (if they were watching their screens...).

It was now 2134 Z and *Bingo!* JA1JRK starts CQing USA on 1908 kHz, listening 1.823 kHz. I figure my spot has cycled through and Rio has seen it. I call on 1.823 kHz and he answers me immediately, with a 559 report. The first-ever North America/East Coast to JA long-path QSO is in the log at 2135 Z and Rio is now calling CQ with no replies. I spot Rio and begin tuning around for more JA callers. After about 10 minutes Toshi, JH5FXP, begins CQing QSX 1803 kHz and I am copying him also at 579. JA1JRK has gone into daylight and has vanished without making any more USA QSOs so I begin calling Toshi. He hears me too and gives a 559 at 2155 Z.

As we sign, I hear Hiro, JA4DND, calling me about 300 Hz up in frequency and I send him a report but he doesn't seem to copy it. I send it again and again without a reply. Just then, Tomio, JA4LXY, calls me over JA4DND and it is obvious he is hearing me better than Hiro is at the moment. I exchange 579 reports with

Tomio at 2201 Z and then go back again to Hiro, who is still calling me. Finally he hears me and copies his report and there are now four JA long-path QSOs in the log!

From 2204 Z to 2212 I listen to JR6PGB call CQ USA QSX on 1805 kHz. He is weaker than the other JAs but a solid 459. I call him until he fades out but never seem to attract his attention. Now the sun has risen all over Japan and it is all over. But I am delighted that I did come down to the shack that day. I listened the next five days straight and heard JH5FXP weakly on the 27th and 29th but that was it. I made no further QSOs into JA during the rest of the 1996/1997 winter season. But it sure was exciting!

About a week later I received a letter from Yasuo, JA3ONB. In it he advised that he was hearing me from 2150 to 2200 Z on 1803.5 to 1805 but couldn't call me because his transmitter didn't work. He also sent me some neat sunrise/sunset charts he had plotted that clearly indicated that there is only a window into Cape Cod for about three weeks each year of about 20 minutes duration. Into my NY QTH, the window is about a week long, with less than 10 minutes duration. So, I guess the strategy of trying this from up north closer to VE1ZZ paid off in spades. I know I will never forget the season of 1996/1997—it provided these and many other thrills that keep me coming back to 160 meters again and again!

CARL HENSON, WB4ZNH

In 1976, still pretty much wet behind the ears, I was planning a DXing vacation. Paul Newberry, N4PN (then W4YWX), talked me into going to Samoa. Martha and I borrowed a Swan linear from Gene Sykes, W4OO, and took our Yaesu FT-101B to Pago Pago. Soon after we arrived, I approached the Public TV station manager about putting our antenna on their tower. The next evening we had a dipole 70 feet up the tower on the peak of a mountain top about a thousand feet above the ocean.

The station closed at 10:00 PM and the transmitter site was locked up tight. We were instructed to get there early and when the TV folks left for the day, they locked us inside. For two or three days I called CQ for hours on end. I could only hear a 20 dB over S9 rush of QRN. But, I also kept hearing dits and dahs in the noise. Once I even imagined I heard a W8. Later, I found out that I had heard W8LRL.

Meanwhile, the Topband world was going crazy! I was being heard all over the world but couldn't hear squat. I finally gave up on that location and moved everything to Larry Gandy's (KS6DV) QTH and finally did work the usual Topband diehards back then, including W1BB. After a week on American Samoa, we flew to Apia and picked up my 5W1BC license. I rushed back to the hotel and got the dipole up just a little ways. There was no good tall place to suspend the antenna. I used my 4BTV as a mast on top of Agie Grey's Hotel, and come to think of it, that was the best use I can think of for a 4BTV vertical.

When I took the radio and other equipment up to the little room for operating, I had too much to carry to take the linear with me on the first trip. I would have to make another trip in order to go get it. Since the sun was just going down, I couldn't stand to wait till I could make the short trip back to the room. So, I hooked up the FT-101B and with a blazing 62 W, called CQ CQ CQ DE 5W1BC 5W1BC K. It had been just a few hours since the call had been issued, and on the absolute first transmission using that call sign, out of the noise came a distinct CW signal. 5W1BC 5W1BC DE W1BB W1BB K.

I still get goose bumps thinking about it! If someday I could say that I was 1/10th the DXer that Stew Perry was, I would be proud. I am content to be one DXer who gave Stew two new ones on 160 meters!

WARD SILVER, N0AX

My best story is about a QRP trip to Easter Island. The XR0Y boys were really cutting a rug on 160 meters in September 1995. I kept hearing all about how everyone had worked them and how good the signals were on 80 and 160. I had just had a major tree fall and my tower wire had been removed to get the mess cleaned up. So I had nothing on 160 at all.

With all the talk, I figured "What the heck, let's put an L back up and just see if I can hear them." A day later, I had a 50 foot up/ 90 foot over piece of #12 wire up between the redwood and the white pine. I was also covered with pine pitch, but that means it's going to work, right? No ground system to speak of, just one three foot piece of brass rod with the coax shield hose-clamped to it. No radials, no nothing!

So I start listening to the expedition about 1300-1400 every morning at sunrise. Anything on 160? Not a peep and time was running out. On one of the last days, I had been tuning on 160 and not hearing anything, so I listened to their SSB operator on 40 phone to see if they were going to move down or something. Nothing but "So and so, you're 59" and I was beginning to doze off. Oh well, guess I missed them, but for some reason I took one more gander at their 160 meter frequency and, low and behold, they were pounding in! I expected to hear a huge pileup come back right away, but the frequency was quiet as they signed off. There was then a five-second debate in my head, could I work them QRP or would I lose the chance to make the QSO entirely?

Oh, why not? Easter Island would be on again someday, anyway. So I called at 5 W and I guess their vertical on the beach was working pretty well because they came back after a minute or so and we got all the information across. I have that card framed on the wall of the shack.

That inverted L has a much better ground system now and I have more countries in the log, but nothing is ever going to compare with that QRP QSO! In general, I think most of my memorable DX QSOs have been made while running QRP. They don't have quite the quantity of my 100-W log entries, but jeepers, they make the hairs on your arm stand up!

PETER BOBEK, DJ8WL

I only rediscovered Topband in 1972 after completing my university studies. At that time we here in DL were only allowed to run 10 W RF out and we had to get our 160-meter permits renewed annually in order to stay on the air. Frequencies were 1815 to 1832 (CW) and 1832 to 1835 (SSB). Due to the power limitations I had to wait until November 1976 to work my first North American station (W2PV).

The most difficult area to work from Western Europe is the Pacific. It's not only 180 degrees away but there is also not much activity from stations with good antennas. Most of the boys out there seem to prefer high-frequency DXing and don't even think of the low bands. The conditions have to be very good to hear them. To work them is something else. I still need KH6 and, for me, my toughest zone has always been Zone 31. Thanks to the efforts of NZ8B (who was at KX6DC then) I did finally manage to complete my WAZ-40 on 160 meters. It was done on October 25, 1988, after trying/running skeds for many days.

My most exciting moments over the years have been:

6Y5IC—I was his first QSO on 160 meters after his passing the exams the day before! Wenty had skeds with his brother G3RFS. He was so surprised to receive a call from Europe that it took him 5 minutes to send my call correctly on CW. I was a new country for him as well.

KX6DC—Of course I shall never forget Jim's efforts to give me my last zone on 160 meters. It was great hearing his "OK" and "QSL."

ZD8TC—Ted patiently transmitted his report for minutes until I was able to pull his signals out of the slow QSB and noise.

FK8CP—I had telephone and FAX communication with Remi just before the QSO to discuss our sked. I never thought it would be so easy!

KC6CW—Mine received my FAX in his hotel on Palau and kept the sked to work me.

JD1AMA—Kat/JH1RES called me one evening on the phone

Fig 10-14—DJ8WL's "Milestones on 160 Meters" chart tracking Peter's success on Topband over the years.

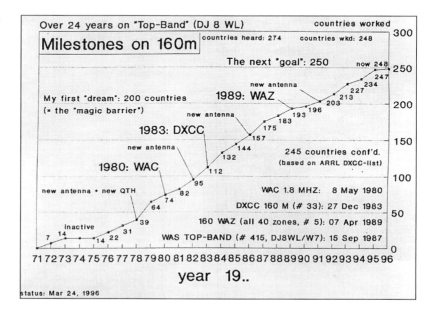

to advise he had set up a sked with JD1AMA for the next day. When I called CQ JA the next evening, I found JD1AMA calling me!

VU4GDG—I never thought this station was genuine!

There are so many memorable moments on 160. I feel obliged to say *thank you* to all, even though it is not possible to list all these exciting moments here.

ROB FLORY, K2WI

Defining my most exciting moments on Topband is really hard as every 160-meter contest is a series of great moments. For example, each new antenna project, if it proves itself to work well, is a great moment. The first time Peter, WW2Y, and I fired up our new four-element array and rode right over K1ZM operating from Cape Cod to DK1NO was a special moment. It let us know our hard work all summer long out in the woods amongst the thorns and ticks had been rewarded.

I think the other one that stands out in my mind happened during the 1993 ARRL 160 Meter Contest when we were operating multioperator from WW2Y's station in Princeton, NJ.

Fig 10-15—Team WW2Y. Rob, K2WI (right) with teammates John, N2NU (center) and Peter, WW2Y. The boys are celebrating their winning score in the 1997 CQ 160-Meter Contest over arch-rival Team W2GD.

In the course of half an hour, I worked seven Kazakh stations and three UA9s! We had never worked UA9 from Peter's station before and only one UN station. This, by the way, was one of those freak openings on 160 meters that is caused by the onset of a solar flare. It's what makes Topband so exciting. As soon as I can figure this band out, I'm going to quit because it won't be as much fun anymore!

CHRIS BURGER, ZS6EZ

If you have been around for a few solar cycles, you have probably been round the DX track a few times. You have seen it all and probably have a QSL collection that would turn the average neophyte green with envy. You are no longer excited by exchanging weather reports with Hans in Hamburg or Toshi in Tokyo. You are no longer impressed by pseudo-contacts with pseudo-DX on a DX net, while Saint Snooky or one of his cohorts stands by to pronounce that the contact has been good. You can hardly remember the excitement you felt when you made your first contact or even your first DXCC! What do you do? You head for Topband!

Most of the really memorable experiences of my ham radio career have been on Topband. There was hearing that first W6 appear from the noise, exchanging reports with him and then listening to him fade from S9 back into the noise, all within 30 seconds. Then there was working just a handful of stations on Topband in a week after trying really hard from Walvis Bay, and then having a massive opening the last morning that my host could even hear through the headset. Then there was working a massive opening from Swaziland with incredibly modest equipment.

The Swaziland experience must certainly stand out as the most memorable. I remember W0ZV saying at the time that it was also his most memorable contact but I have heard him say twice since then that other contacts have taken its place. But, for me, it continues to stand out as a once-in-a-lifetime experience. At the time, I owned a Heathkit SB-220 amplifier. Because it did not cover Topband, I borrowed another amplifier for my 1988 Swaziland trip. The antenna was a Butternut HF2V sitting on a tin roof with extensive top loading and lots of radials. Judging by

Fig 10-16—Some mouth-watering 160-meter QSLs belonging to K1MEM.

the input impedance, the ground plane was doing a great job and the antenna's performance should have been very close to that of a full-sized vertical. I completed the antenna installation during the night and its first test would be with the dawn opening.

I was running stations on 80 meters when I noticed that light was starting to show on the eastern horizon. Signals were reasonably loud and I was looking forward to a good opening on 160 meters. I announced that I would be going to Topband and started rapidly rewiring the station. I installed the borrowed amplifier and tried to tune it up. There was no way I could get it to load into the awkward impedance presented by the vertical. I eventually gave up and tried to fire the exciter directly into the antenna. The SWR caused the exciter to cut back to about 30 W output, but I decided to call CQ anyway, since there might have been one or two locals that would be interested in a contact. I called CQ a few times and announced that I would be listening up.

When the receiver came back on, there was a massive pileup on my listening frequency. I thought there must have been another station listening there but I decided to try to work one of them to see what would happen. Sure enough, WB2Q came back to me! I then proceeded to work several dozen stations in that opening with stations as far west as Colorado finding their way into my log.

I went back to 80 meters and several of those that I had worked on 160 commented on the great signals. I mentioned that I had used only 30 W. It appears that my statement was straining credibility somewhat as I received two QSL cards commenting that I had had a great signal for only 300 W. During the remainder of that week I continued to try to work stations on 160 meters using the 30 W to the vertical. I worked several stations each night but nothing close to that first morning's opening.

We really are far away from everything down here in Southern Africa and I have spent many nights listening to static with not a single signal on the band. But, whenever I start losing heart, I think back to that one morning. And, I decide all over again that it is all worth it!

Chapter 11

Simple and Effective 160-Meter DXing Transmit Antennas

Reading about the exploits of others working DX on 160 meters can be enjoyable, but it is much more *fun* when you can join the pileups yourself. There are two very simple transmit antennas you can use to get started on Topband and both of these will generate a very effective transmit signal, even at exciter power levels. Should you be fortunate enough to have a kW amplifier available to help cut through the 160-meter QRN, then you will find either of these antenna systems very much to your liking.

We will discuss each approach in detail, since either will provide that all-important low-angle takeoff, so critical for working DX on the low bands. Remember, many antennas will work on 160 meters but the trick is to try to avoid the simple low dipole or low Inverted-V approach. Low horizontal antennas tend to shoot most of your radiated power straight up. This is of little utility when attempting to work DX on 160 meters.

You should also avoid, if possible, very short verticals or commercial multi-band verticals with those outrageous claims about how effective radiators they are on Topband. If you are serious about having fun on 160 meters, there is a far better way to do it and it is probably more cost effective as well.

THE "LOAD-YOUR-TOWER" APPROACH

If you have a typical 50 to 70-foot tower with a tribander and/ or a "shorty-forty" atop it, then you can be *loud* on 160 meters by laying down a respectable ground radial system and feeding the tower as a "folded unipole." This system has been used here at K1ZM for many years with excellent results.

The ground system part is pretty basic. You will need to lay down at least 32 $1/4$-wave radials (each 130 feet long) from the base of the tower in all directions. Sixty-four radials are better still and 120 radials is the standard for commercial AM broadcast work. A 120-wire ground radial system is close to ideal, but don't be overly concerned if you cannot accommodate such a system at your location. Less-aggressive radial systems will work—and work well—as long as some of the radials are over 66 feet long.

The radials can be bent around buildings or around property lines and they do not necessarily have to be uniformly arrayed equally in all directions of the compass azimuth. The important point is to lay down as much wire as you can under your tower, given your specific situation and limitations. On Cape Cod, for example, I used to use a vertical system with no radials at all from about 190 to 350 degrees on the compass. This was because my tower was against my house and this precluded any radials at all in the directions that went directly through the house. What I did instead to compensate was to put those missing radials on the other side of the tower, over 400 in all, from 355 degrees through about 185 degrees, where I again ran into the foundation of the house and had to stop.

So, you need not be fooled into thinking that a vertical will not work DX if it has only 16 or 32 radials under it. It will work a lot of DX, but simply will not be as efficient a radiator as it might be were a full complement of 120 radials used instead. With a kW amplifier going into it, you can still work a ton of DX on 160 meters with such an antenna!

To feed a ground-mounted (non-insulated base) tower system, please refer to **Fig 11-1**. One of the most basic feed systems I often use is to run three drop wires in a triangular "cage" from the tower's base up to the top of the tower. These are made from #14 stranded THHN electrical wire, available from any Home Depot outlet. I offset the drop wires from the tower about

Fig 11-1—K1ZM's approach to making cross arms for the three-wire cage feed. Note the lack of ground radials for 180° of the compass. Weatherproofing of the matching unit is accomplished using a Rubbermaid "Roughneck" box with lid.

15 inches on "tomato poles" constructed in the shape of a cross.

The "cross" is made by cutting off an 8-inch piece from each pole and then placing it at right angles to a 26-inch piece of tomato pole. The 8 inch piece of the pole I usually screw onto the 26-inch piece about 6 inches down from its top. The completed cross pieces are then placed inside Rohn 25 or 45 tower so they can be taped to the horizontal support members of the tower and to the rails of the tower for physical and mechanical support. When done correctly, you wind up with about 11 inches of pole inside the tower and about 15 inches of pole (the end with the cross on it) sticking outside the tower. The cross ends of the pole, in the shape of a triangle, thus form the support arms to hold the three cage drop wires in position 15 inches off the face of the tower.

I then pass the drop wires through pre-drilled holes in the

ends of cross parts of the arms to keep the wires in position as they run up the side of the tower. With a 70-foot tower, four sets of crosses spaced every 18 feet or so work very nicely to keep the cage wires at a distance of 15 inches from the tower. It is easiest, by the way, to first put the standoff poles on the tower and then haul the three cage wires up the tower with you. This allows gravity to work in your favor as you climb back down the tower passing the wires through the holes in the ends of the crossarms as you go.

At the top of the tower near the rotator, the three cage wires should be twisted together and then shorted to one of the tower legs. A hose clamp works very well for this purpose. I tape up this connection after completing tuning of the system.

At the bottom of the tower, the three cage drop wires are again hooked together and fixed to the output side of the matching system depicted in **Fig 11-2A**. The matching system required usually can be as simple as a series 750-pF vacuum variable with a 5 kV rating. This will handle a kW power level safely.

Wiring up the matching system is very simple as it is only necessary to hook the center conductor of your 50-Ω coax feed line to one side of the vacuum-variable matching capacitor and the three drop wires tied together to the other side of the vacuum capacitor. The coax ground shield of the feed line connects to the radial ground system, which is also connected to the base of one of your tower legs, again with a hose clamp. See **Fig 11-3** for a photograph of the completed shunt-fed tower system.

The matching system should be built inside a suitable enclosure to protect it from the elements. For this, I usually use a Rubbermaid "Roughneck" heavy-duty plastic box with a removable cover. To get into and out of the box I use an SO-239 female coaxial connector mounted on one side of the Rubbermaid enclosure and a long $1/4$-inch *brass* screw with a *brass* wingnut mounted on the other side. The SO-239 makes it easy to connect your feed line to the matching unit and it also simplifies SWR checking and tuning. The brass screw with the brass wingnut makes it simple to connect the three drop wires to the matching system. Brass is specifically recommended for this application because it doesn't rust and brass is far more appropriate for RF. Steel is a poor conductor relative to brass and it heats up at kW

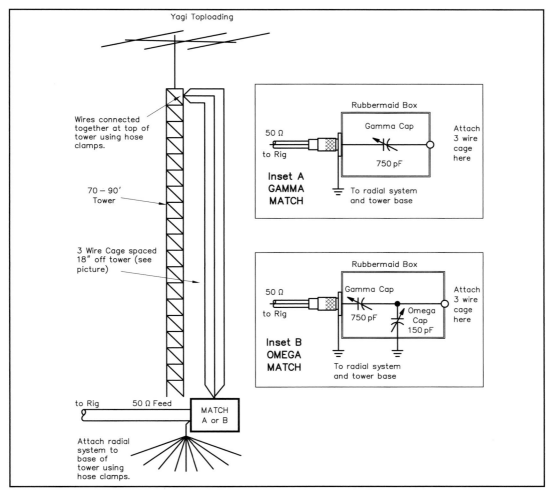

Fig 11-2—Drawing of a shunt-fed tower with a "cage" feed system. The three cage wires are separated from the tower and from each other using four cross-shaped frames up the side of the tower.

power levels. (If you happen to catch Bob, K3UL, on the band some night you might ask him about the fire he had inside his matching box one time because he used a steel screw instead of brass. It is a great 160 story.)

Tuning the system is very simple. I prefer to use an Autek RF-1 RF Analyst at the point where the feed line enters the SO-239 matching network input, but tuning can be done in the

Fig 11-3—The completed 60-foot high shunt-fed tower system, with a TV antenna for top loading. Obviously, a 20-meter Yagi or a tribander beam would give even better top loading!

shack at the rig using 50 W or so output power if you like. Start by adjusting the vacuum capacitor for minimum SWR at your desired operating frequency. For DX work on 160 meters, tuning up your system around 1830 kHz is a good choice, since this is about the center of the usable DX band these days.

If a dip is noted on the SWR meter, but the SWR is still higher than about 1.3:1, then it may be necessary to climb the tower to reposition the tap point where the cage wires come together and are shorted to the tower leg. For this, a clip lead can be used. Try coming down the tower a few feet from the hose clamp and use the clip lead to connect one wire of the cage to one of the zigzag support rungs of the tower. It will be necessary to skin the wire first when making this connection if THHN electrical hookup wire was used for the cage. Retweak the vacuum capacitor again and check to see the new SWR value at 1830. By moving the tap point and readjusting the gamma capacitor in combination it should be possible to achieve an acceptable SWR value pretty quickly. Once you have found the correct tap point and finished your tuning, be sure to remove the clip lead and make a proper, soldered connection from the cage to a tower leg using a hose clamp.

If moving the tap point is not convenient, there is a "lazy man's" alternate approach to solving the problem, but it requires another vacuum capacitor to do it. Instead of using only a series Gamma-match capacitor, one can try an Omega-match feed system. Here one places the additional Omega capacitor between the drop wire side of the Gamma capacitor and the ground radial system. (If you have purchased the larger size Rubbermaid "Roughneck" box for your enclosure, you will find it no problem to fit two vacuum capacitors inside.)

Using this approach, one leaves the cage tap point alone and merely tunes both vacuum capacitors in harmony (first, one a bit, and then the other) in order to achieve a perfect 1:1 SWR. This can be done in a matter of minutes. The Omega capacitor usually needs to be from 150 to 300 pF in value, again with a 5 kV rating. Please refer to Fig 11-2B for a drawing of the alternate Omega matching system.

In many cases, I have found the Gamma feed (one series capacitor) will match a vertical to an acceptable SWR quite easily. However, if the tower is an odd height or if a more complex impedance is present, the Omega capacitor system solves the problem easily without having to monkey around with changing the tap point of the drop wire cage up the tower.

You will find that a system with 32 or 64 radials under it will provide at least 50 to 60 kHz of usable bandwidth on 160 meters. This means you should be able to work from the low band edge of 1800 kHz up through about 1860 kHz with an SWR below 2:1.

This is where most of the DX is on 160 meters anyway, so if you have already erected such a transmit system, then take a look now at the chapter on 160 meters receive antennas. You are ready to work the DX—you only need to install a proper receiving antenna with which to hear them!

THE BASIC ¹/₄-WAVE INVERTED-L ANTENNA

If you do not have a tower, don't worry—you can still work DX on 160 meters. W1BB didn't have a real tower at his home QTH either, so he installed the simple inverted-L antenna I'm going to describe next to solve his transmit signal problems. A diagram drawn by Stew of his version of a transmit L antenna appears in **Fig 11-4**. This version is longer than a quarter wavelength and is tuned to resonance with a series variable capacitor. It worked well for Stew and it will work wonders for you too.

In fact, there probably have been more than a hundred 160-meter DXCCs made around the world over the past 15 years with the inverted-L antenna. As they say, the proof is in the pudding. Please refer to **Fig 11-5** for a diagram of an inverted L layout that is a quarter-wave long. Both Stew's approach and the Fig 11-5 approach will work well.

The ¹/₄-wave inverted L is actually a *poor man's vertical*, since it is partly a vertical radiator and partly a horizontal radiator. Its total length is around ¹/₄ wave, or 133 feet on 160 meters. The vertical component is determined by the height of any available support you may have at your QTH. The radiator itself is usually made from #12 or #14 stranded THHN wire, which can be found at any Home Depot outlet or at your favorite electrical supply store.

Most hams without a tower usually look for a tall tree from which to suspend their inverted L, and some even employ a small 40-foot mast or use fiberglass fishing poles if no suitable tree is available on their property. For this discussion, we will assume you have located at least a 40-foot tall support structure of some kind and have managed to suspend 40 feet (or more) of wire vertically, with the remainder of it (93 feet) tied off in a horizontal plane to some suitable point.

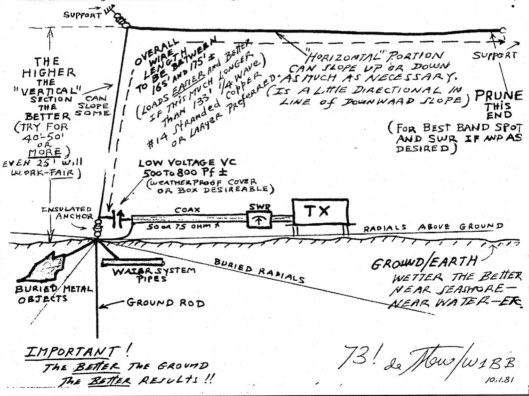

Fig 11-4—Excerpt from January 10, 1981, W1BB 160-Meter Bulletin showing his Inverted-L antenna. This antenna is made longer than an electrical quarter wavelength so that the feed-point resistance is close to 50 Ω after the series capacitor is tuned for resonance.

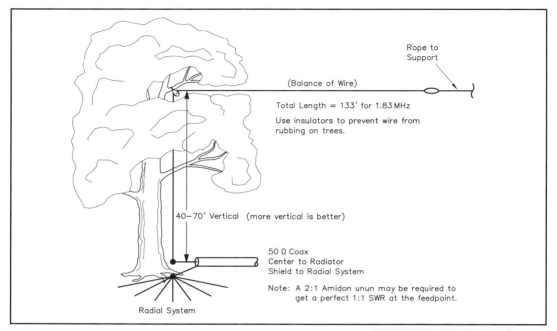

Rope to
Support

(Balance of Wire)

Total Length = 133' for 1.83 MHz

Use insulators to prevent wire from
rubbing on trees.

40–70' Vertical (more vertical is better)

50 Ω Coax
Center to Radiator
Shield to Radial System

Note: A 2:1 Amidon unun may be required to
get a perfect 1:1 SWR at the feedpoint.

Radial System

Fig 11-5—K1ZM's quarter-wave Inverted-L antenna. He uses a 2:1 Amidon UNUN matching transformer to achieve a 1:1 SWR.

As with any other vertical for 160 meters, the inverted L requires a ground radial system to work properly. The same rules and suggestions made previously for feeding your tower apply. Try to use at least 16 or 32 radials under the vertical part of the inverted L—more if you can manage them.

One of the nice things about the basic ¼-wave inverted-L antenna is that you can usually feed it directly with 50-Ω coax line—a matching network is usually not required for a ¼-wave radiator. This makes tuning the antenna a breeze!

The easiest way to proceed is to first set up the radiator and initially make it around 140 feet in length. Then lay down your final radial system under it. Now you are ready for tuning. Using a portable SWR Analyzer at the feed point of the L or by using the SWR meter on your rig in the shack, find the resonant point of the inverted L. Normally, this will be down below 1800 kHz and possibly even as low as around 1700 kHz.

Now, trim the end of the horizontal *tail* of the antenna by lowering the far end of the radiator from its support. Do this a little bit at a time so you don't overshoot 1832 kHz, which should be your objective. I usually start with about two feet at a time and progressively cut off less and less as I near the desired point of resonance. Hoist the tail back up in the air after making each cut.

Once you have trimmed your inverted L at 1832 kHz you will most likely wind up with an SWR of less than 2:1, but probably not a perfect 1:1. Most ¼-wave inverted-L antennas have a characteristic impedance of from 22 to 30 Ω at their feed point if the vertical component of the L is 40 to 60 feet high.

If the impedance is higher than that range, you probably have higher ground losses than you would like. If your SWR comes out close to 1:1, then you could go ahead and use it—or you could improve your ground system. If you find your SWR closer to 2.0:1 at resonance on 1832 kHz, the ground losses are probably reasonable. You might wish to purchase an Amidon Associates UNUN. UNUNs are made with varying input and output impedance taps and cost around $55 from Amidon Associates. Amidon makes a great one with 22/25-Ω impedance taps on one side and a 50-Ω tap on the other side. And, they have coax female SO-239 connectors on either side, making it a snap to put these little devices out at the antenna in between your feed line and the input side of the L radiator.

All one needs is a double-male coax connector assuming you have made a box with an SO-239 female coax connector on it for connection at your Inverted-L feed point. I do this as a matter of course on my Inverted-L antennas as it is not good practice to be soldering the feed line coax directly to the base of the antenna and to the ground radial system.

At K1ZM, I use a plastic Radio Shack box about the size of a pack of cigarettes with an SO-239 female coaxial connector mounted on it to make my feed-point connections. This allows for a quick disconnect of the feed line at the feed point of my inverted L when necessary. It also simplifies insertion of an RF-1 RF Analyst or SWR bridge for tuning purposes. Pigtail wires exit the box through small holes for the connections to the vertical radiator wire and to the ground-radial system.

I usually secure the box to a wooden stake hammered into the ground at the feed point. The stake keeps tension on the vertical radiator wire when the wind blows. You should also tape the feed line to the bottom of the stake as a strain relief for the coax connection to the box. This also provides an easy place to insert an Amidon 2:1 UNUN at the feed point to keep your transmitter happy. The Amidon UNUNs easily handle 1.5 kW with no problem.

If you happen to have a 500-pF/5 kV vacuum-variable capacitor handy, the expense of the UNUN can be avoided by employing the W1BB method of matching an inverted L in Fig 11-4. Stew found that by making the overall length about 180 feet in length instead of a $^1/_4$ wave, he could insert a series capacitor between his coax feed line and the vertical radiator wire to achieve a 1:1 SWR. In this case, the capacitor is connected between the center conductor of the 50-Ω feed line and the vertical radiator wire.

The capacitor should be placed in a weatherproof Rubbermaid type enclosure and the coax shield of the feed line should be connected to the ground radial system. The feed line will be connected to the SO-239 female on the weatherproof box, the center pin of which goes to one side of the vacuum cap. The vertical radiator wire will go to a brass screw on the other side of the box, connected internally to the other side of the vacuum capacitor. As was the case with the Gamma capacitor described previously in the tower matching unit, the series capacitor is floating with respect to earth ground.

The principle that allows this feed system to work is that an inverted L longer than a quarter wavelength causes the feed-point resistance to rise close to 50 Ω and the feed-point reactance to look inductive. Inserting the series tuning capacitor at the feed point cancels out the inductive reactance. The result is a good match to the 50-Ω feed line.

MOVING ON UP—HIGH PERFORMANCE TRANSMIT ARRAYS FOR 160 METERS

Both the feed-your-tower and the single inverted L approaches offer upgrade possibilities if you want to expand and improve your system someday. Towers and inverted Ls can be phased for directivity and gain. They also can be deployed in Four-Square arrays for a *top of the food chain* antenna system on 160 meters!

When you are ready to think about expanding your system, I suggest you pick up a copy of ON4UN's fine book on the subject entitled *Low Band DXing*. John Devoldere describes many of the approaches by which this may be done. His book is also an ARRL publication that I refer to often. Most serious DXers know that John has one of the finest 160-meter antenna systems in the world—there is much even an expert can learn from reading John's work.

In this section, I'll describe some systems that could be constructed in a short period of time. I've used some of these myself at K1ZM and others have been employed with great success at other successful Topband stations, such as WW2Y by Peter Hutter and Rob Flory, K2WI.

The most practical approach to achieve gain on 160 meters is through the use of vertical radiators in combination, since rotatable Yagis and super-high horizontal systems are pretty much out of the question because of mechanical considerations. The ¼-wave inverted L is an excellent building block for a 160-meter directive array, since it can be suspended from a tree as low as 40 to 50 feet high. Many amateurs are fortunate enough to have a number of trees favorably located for use as supports in a multiple-vertical array. The inverted-L approach sure beats the expense of erecting full-sized ¼-wave radiators made out of towers.

SIMPLE TWO-VERTICAL PHASED ARRAYS

For this discussion, I will assume an East Coast USA location, where the goal is gain and directivity into Europe. It would also be a plus to have gain into the South Pacific to make it easier to work VK/ZL and KH6 stations.

There are a number of ways to design a two-vertical array. The approach you select will be a function of the supports available and the size of your parcel of land. If you are limited by land size, ¼-wavelength spacing between the two radiators is probably a good choice for a basic system. In this case, the bases of the two inverted-Ls should be set 130 feet apart, with the front or leading vertical aimed northeast on an azimuth of about 50°. The rear vertical should be positioned in a southwest direction at about 230°.

A line drawn between the bases of the two verticals would yield a northeast/southwest alignment when firing off the ends of the system. The horizontal top portions of each inverted L should be facing each other for best symmetry in the system. The two top portions are often suspended from a horizontal, non-conducting catenary hung between the two supporting trees.

When laying the bases out on the ground using a magnetic compass, don't forget to take into account the deviation at your specific location from True North. In New England, for example, True North is 15° to the east of Magnetic North, since the magnetic variation is 15° west.

Just as in the case of a single inverted-L antenna, a proper ground radial system is mandatory under each radiator. For the two-vertical array, the number of radials under each radiator should be identical, to achieve a balanced system. The use of 33 or 66 radials under each inverted L will yield good performance. It is *not* a good idea to have 66 radials under one inverted L and only 8, 16 or 33 radials under the second inverted L! Multiple element vertical arrays work best with a completely symmetrical design.

Fig 11-6A shows the layout of the two-vertical array. Phasing lines A and B can be made of $^1/_4$-wave 50-Ω RG-213 or equivalent. Remember to take into account the velocity factor of the specific coaxial line employed and trim the $^1/_4$-wave lines to final length using a grid dip meter. As a guide only, RG-213 coax has a nominal velocity factor of around 0.66. It produces a physical length for an electrical quarter-wave at about 86 feet, 4 inches at 1.830 MHz. Your coax may have a slightly different velocity factor, so it is very important to achieve precision using a grid-dip meter when determining the length of these phasing lines.

Combining the two radiators to achieve directivity and forward gain can be done in several ways. To make the array fire northeast, for example, it is necessary to create a 90° excitation lag at radiator A such that radiator B receives excitation 90° before A does. This is easily accomplished with a commercial 90° hybrid device, such as the Comtek Systems ACB-4 unit. Normally, you mount the ACB-4 external head on a short mast stuck into the ground and position it midway between the two radiators. Phasing lines A and B connect to the hybrid using PL-259 coaxial connectors, as described in the Comtek

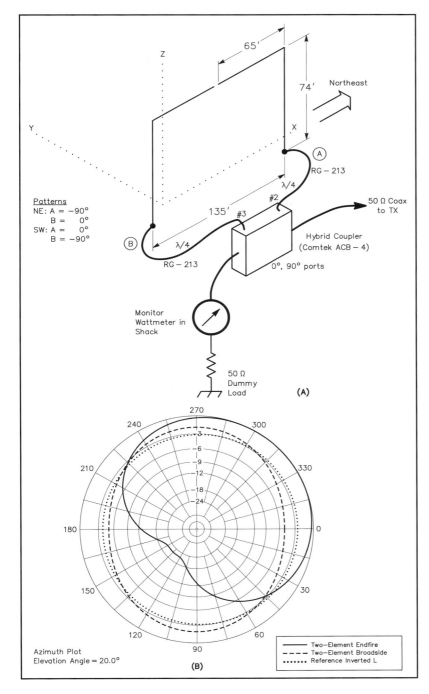

Fig 11-6—At A, diagram of "foot print" of two-element 160-meter phased array. Not shown are the ground radials required at the base of each radiator. The two top "tails" for each radiator are usually suspended from a non-conducting catenary between the two trees used as supports. A Comtek ACB-4 hybrid coupler is used to provide switchable phasing of 0° and 90° for the two radiators. This switches the beam from northeast to southwest. The 50-Ω dummy load (with wattmeter in the shack) is used to monitor the power diverted to the dummy load because of imbalances in the system. At B, azimuthal response of the two-element phased array for end-fire phasing into either the northeast or southwest directions, compared to broadside phasing into northwest or southeast directions and to a single inverted L used as a reference. The ground characteristics for this plot, as well as all others following, is typical of New England: very poor and rocky.

instructions. Remote switching of the 90° hybrid is achieved with a 12-V control line. This places the 90° phase lag alternatively in series with phasing line A or line B to switch direction of the beam. When the 90° excitation lag is placed in series with phasing line B, the array fires in the southwest direction.

Such a system allows for essentially unidirectional patterns northeast or southwest and develops about 3 dB of forward gain compared to a single vertical radiator, and a nominal front-to-back ratio of about 12 to 15 dB. See Fig 11-6B. The Comtek units sell for around $340 and also require a dummy load (not supplied with the unit) to dissipate safely any power imbalance resulting from mismatched (dissimilar) radiators. Comtek Systems is located in Charlotte, North Carolina, and can be reached at (704) 542-4808.

As always, there is another approach for the ham on a budget who can't afford a fancy Comtek box. This approach is depicted in **Fig 11-7A**. Here, an electrical $^1/_2$ wavelength of 50-Ω coaxial cable is inserted in series with either phasing line A or phasing line B. A simple T coaxial connector mated with a PL-258 barrel connector is used to hook up a 50-Ω coaxial feed line going to the transmitter.

The $^1/_2$-wavelength 50-Ω line (nominally 172 feet, 8 inches for RG-213, which has a velocity factor of 0.66) produces a 180° excitation lag in one of the two radiators, depending upon its placement and forces a bidirectional pattern northeast and southwest simultaneously. The resulting gain is on the order of 3 dB referenced to a single vertical radiator but in this case it is usable gain both to Europe and to VK/ZL simultaneously. Nulls are produced to the northwest and southeast. You can expect to see about 12 to 15 dB of reduction for incoming signals from those directions. See Fig 11-7B.

You can take advantage of an additional feature when feeding the system above. The array can be made to fire bidirectionally to the northwest and southeast simultaneously by eliminating the $^1/_2$-wave line. You would simply remove the $^1/_2$-wave line and connect phasing lines A and B to the T connector directly. Due to the relatively close spacing of the two radiators at only $^1/_4$ wavelength, the resulting in-phase broadside pattern only produces about 1 dB of bidirectional gain compared to a single radiator. This is better than nothing and represents almost a *freebie*, thrown in for little additional effort.

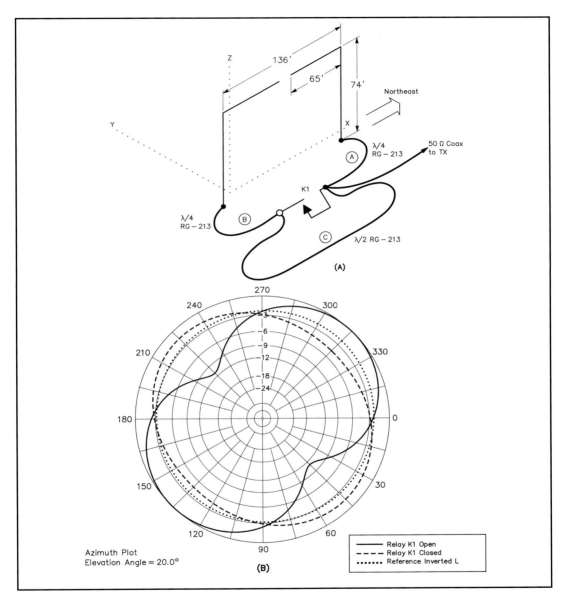

Fig 11-7—At A, footprint of two-element, quarter-wave spaced phased array with simple relay switching system instead of Comtek hybrid combiner box. With relay K1 closed, the two feed coaxes are connected in parallel for a broadside beam pattern; with K1 open, an end-fire pattern results because of λ/2 feed line in series with coax B. At B, azimuthal plot comparisons showing these patterns compared to that of a single reference inverted L.

Pattern reversal can be remotely switched from inside the shack using a 12-V SPST relay housed in a Radio Shack aluminum project box. Be sure to use a quality relay with contacts rated at 10 to 15 A for the switching, and make sure you weatherproof the box well. Never switch the pattern while transmitting, since such *hot switching* at a kW power level will fry the relay contacts in short order!

When you switch pattern from bidirectional end-fire northeast or southwest to bidirectional broadside northwest/southeast with such a system, there will be definite pattern nulls found, averaging 12 to 15 dB. This can be helpful in some situations, particularly on receive. It should be noted that in the winter months, when thunderstorm activity is decreased in the Northern Hemisphere, this is a remarkably quiet RX antenna as well.

WHAT IF I HAVE A LITTLE MORE LAND?

The principles of the two-radiator array just described also lend themselves quite nicely to other spacing distances between the two radiators and to other physical layouts on the ground. If more land is available and suitable supports exist in the right places for the two inverted Ls, then try the layout in **Fig 11-8A**.

Here, the two radiators are spaced $5/8$ wavelength or 336 feet apart. To optimize pattern and gain into Europe and into the Pacific, the bases need to be positioned northwest and southeast at about 330° and 150° azimuth. Note that this is very different from the azimuths needed for the pair of verticals spaced $1/4$-wave apart. At the $5/8$-wave spacing, the $1/4$-wavelength phasing lines used previously at A and B will not reach between the two radiators, so $3/4$-wave lines, constructed from RG-213 50-Ω coax, are used instead. The nominal length for these lines using 0.66 velocity factor cable is 259 feet for each.

At a $5/8$-wave spacing, if you feed the radiators in phase using a T connector with no $1/2$-wave delay line, you can achieve about 5 dB of gain over a single vertical radiator. This pattern is bidirectional in the northeast/southwest directions. If $1/2$-wave spacing (266 feet) is employed instead of $5/8$-wave, the resulting broadside gain will be on the order of around 4 dB over a single vertical radiator.

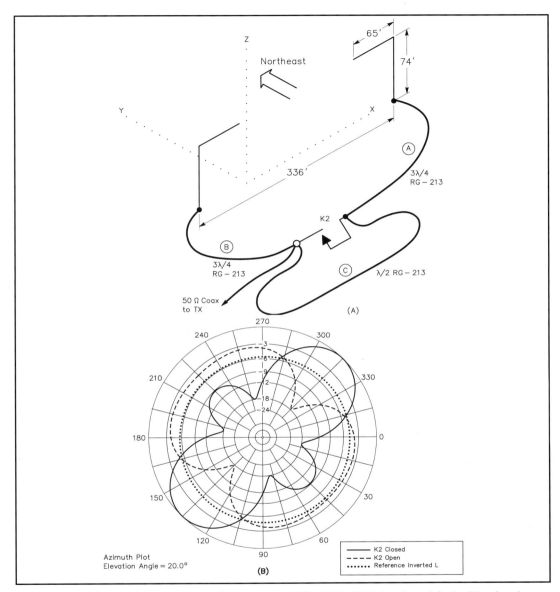

Fig 11-8—At A, two inverted-L radiators spaced by 5λ/8 (336 feet) and fed with simple relay system. At B, the azimuth patterns for K2 open, where the directivity is end fire, and for K2 closed, where the directivity is broadside. For comparison, the azimuth pattern for a reference single inverted L is overlaid on the same plot. Note that the end-fire directivity does "fill in the gaps" in coverage to the northwest and southeast, but it is about 4 dB down from the switchable broadside directions northeast and southwest.

To make the array in Fig 11-8A fire northwest/southeast in a bidirectional end-fire pattern, the $\frac{1}{2}$-wave delay line again is inserted, just as it was before in the earlier example. As before, the same remote switching relay box can be used to reverse the pattern. With the $\frac{1}{2}$-wave delay line inserted in series with either one of the radiators, the nominal gain is about 2 dB over a single radiator. The pattern will be in the northwest and southeast directions simultaneously. Pattern nulls of about 15 dB should be observed when compared to the in-phase pattern northeast/southwest.

One word of caution should be noted when using this half-wave-spaced alternative to a pair of verticals spaced a $\frac{1}{4}$ wave. The placement of the vertical portions of each radiator is more important with $\frac{5}{8}$ and $\frac{1}{2}$-wave spacing. The extra gain derived with the wider spacing comes from squeezing the forward and reverse lobes of the system to make a tighter azimuthal pattern. This means that it is more critical to point the array in the direction desired.

A FEW IDEAS FOR THE REALLY AMBITIOUS

In order to move further up the transmit "food chain," one must look beyond arrays with only two radiators. The approach most often taken by the truly hard-core Topband operators is to use arrays with four radiators. One of the more popular systems employed is the classic *Four-Square array*, which was developed and perfected by Fred Collins, W1FC, and Dana Atchley, W1CF. The layout of a Four-Square array using inverted-L antennas is shown in **Fig 11-9A**.

The sides of a Four Square are laid out using $\frac{1}{4}$-wave spacing or about 130 feet between the bases of each radiator. The diagonals of the square require around 190 feet of space. In this system, typical operation is to combine the four radiators using a suitable hybrid coupler producing 0°, 90° and 180° outputs. Again, the Comtek Systems ACB-4 is an excellent choice for such a system and has proven to be an excellent performer over the years at K1ZM, K1KI, W4DR and other contest-oriented stations in the USA with 160-meter Four Squares in operation.

In a classic $\frac{1}{4}$-wave spaced Four-Square array, the four

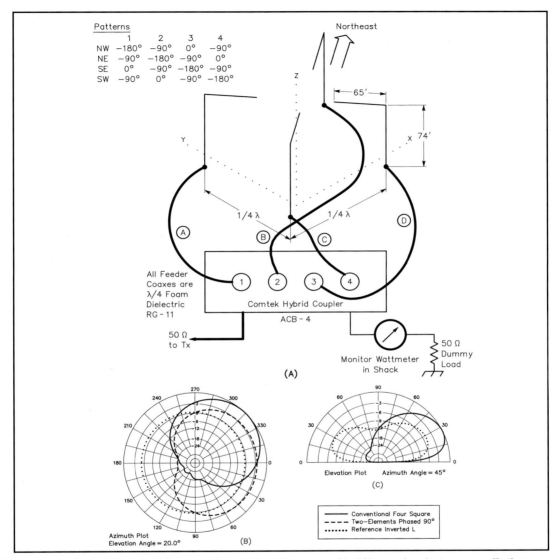

Patterns

	1	2	3	4
NW	−180°	−90°	0°	−90°
NE	−90°	−180°	−90°	0°
SE	0°	−90°	−180°	−90°
SW	−90°	0°	−90°	−180°

Northeast

65'

x 74'

Z

Y

1/4 λ   1/4 λ

Ⓐ   Ⓑ   Ⓒ   Ⓓ

All Feeder
Coaxes are
λ/4 Foam
Dielectric
RG - 11

1   2   3   4

Comtek Hybrid Coupler

ACB - 4

50 Ω
to Tx

Monitor Wattmeter
in Shack

50 Ω
Dummy
Load

(A)

Azimuth Plot
Elevation Angle = 20.0°

(B)

Elevation Plot   Azimuth Angle = 45°

(C)

——— Conventional Four Square
– – – Two–Elements Phased 90°
· · · · · Reference Inverted L

Fig 11-9—At A, footprint of conventional Four Square, with λ/4 spacing between radiating elements. Note that the top tails point toward each other to maintain symmetry in the system. Note the excellent rearward response of this array. The Comtek ACB-4 hybrid coupler is used to control the amplitude and phase of the feeder coax currents. A wattmeter located in the shack is used to monitor the imbalance currents that are dumped into the 50-Ω dummy load. At B, azimuth plots are shown comparing the Four Square to an array with two elements spaced 1/4 λ and fed with 90 degree phasing for end-fire directivity. As usual, a reference single inverted L is included for comparison. At C, the elevation response of the Four Square is compared to that of a single reference inverted L.

vertical radiators are fed from the hybrid coupler through electrically ¼-wavelength 70-Ω foam-dielectric phasing lines having a velocity factor of 0.78 or 0.80. Foam dielectric coaxial cable must be used in this case so that these runs will span the physical distance from the exact center of the array (where the hybrid coupler sits) to each of the four radiators at the sides of the square. Polyethylene-dielectric coax of 0.66 velocity factor will not span this distance when the lines are trimmed to proper electrical length because the velocity factor of such coax is only 0.66. Any suitable 50-Ω coaxial line, such as RG-213, can be used from the transmitter to connect into the hybrid.

The real workhorse of the Four-Square system is the hybrid coupler unit. This handles the current division among the four radiators and produces the proper phase angle outputs required to produce gain. The phase angles need to be held to tight tolerances to derive maximum cancellation among the radiators. The Comtek ACB-4 achieves this with precision toroids and capacitance values.

Since a Four-Square fires across its diagonals during operation (and not down the sides), the hybrid is connected to the radiators such that they typically receive excitation at −180°, −90°, −90° and 0° phase with respect to each other. As indicated in Fig 11-9A, the array will fire northeast when the northeast radiator is lagged at −180°, the northwest and southeast radiators are lagged at −90° and when the southwest radiator is fed at 0° phase.

Switching of the pattern to make the array fire northwest, southeast or southwest is achieved remotely from inside the shack by means of an array controller provided by Comtek Systems. A three-wire line (not supplied) connects the controller to the remote hybrid unit with relay switching at 12 V.

As noted previously, a dummy load is required with this system in order to safely dissipate any mismatched "kickback" power that may be created by dissimilar radiators. The dummy load may remain outside at the hybrid unit in a weatherproof enclosure but it is preferable to run some RG-8X type coax into the shack instead. This allows one to insert a forward power meter in series with the dummy load to monitor ongoing performance of the system during operation. By measuring normal values of kickback power for each of the array's four directions and saving them for future reference, it can easily be determined when a failure has occurred somewhere in the system. Should a failure occur, it will normally show up immediately at the power meter going into the dummy load, showing some value other than the typical value.

Examples of such failures can include water seeping into a phasing line, failure of a relay inside the hybrid coupler, a tree branch brushing up against a radiator, a radiator falling down or even a squirrel or woodchuck taking a bite out of a piece of coax. (Yes, all of the above have happened at K1ZM at one time or another, so placing the dummy load inside the shack and monitoring ongoing operation of the system is well worth the effort.)

Those fortunate enough to be using a true, full-sized Four-Square array on 160 meters constructed out of Rohn 25 tower with elevated bases and elevated radial systems already know what superb systems these are. Or, alternatively, you can tell yourself when you listen to their signals. A few known to be in operation today include Dave, AAØRS (G3SZA), and John, WØUN, in Colorado. Bob, W4DR, in Virginia is another. A picture of Dave's system can be found in the potpourri chapter of this book.

Since few among us will ever have the luxury of a Rohn tower type of Four-Square array on 160 meters, we need to touch on an important design modification required when using $1/4$-wave inverted-Ls as radiators. In fact, such a system will come up to within a fraction of a dB of the gain of a system using $1/4$-wave high towers, providing that the system is laid out in a symmetrical manner.

When you construct such a system in trees using inverted Ls as radiators, the use of 50-Ω $1/4$-wave phasing lines from the hybrid to the radiators will probably provide a better match for the system than will 70-Ω coax. This is because the characteristic impedance of a $1/4$-wave inverted L with a typical 40 to 50 foot vertical height is on the order of 22 to 26 Ω at its feed point. When transformed at the far end of a 50-Ω $1/4$-wavelength phasing line, you will typically see between 61 to 69 Ω presented to the hybrid. Thus, out of the hybrid, the actual SWR presented to the transmitter at the end of the 50-Ω feed line winds up being on the order of 1.3:1, which is very acceptable. So, remember this simple note—use 70-Ω phasing lines on a Four-Square employing true vertical radiators. Use 50-Ω

phasing lines on Four-Squares constructed of $^1/_4$-wavelength inverted L radiators.

VARIATIONS ON THE CLASSIC FOUR SQUARE

Don't be afraid to experiment with designs other than textbook systems. For example, if you have a *very* tall tower, put 40 foot crossarms at the 150 foot level and hang four wire verticals 138 feet in length for your radiators. Make the footprint at the ground level into the textbook spacing for the sides and the diagonals and lay down four identical radial systems and feed the system with 70-Ω phasing lines as described. Hook up a Comtek hybrid and you have a Four Square! It will have less than perfect gain and front-to-back ratio, but the system works awfully well nonetheless.

Tom, K1KI, has tried another adaptation of the Four Square from a tall tower positioned over sloping ground. He hangs wire radiators from rope catenaries sloping toward the surrounding trees. He slopes one of the four wires down a hill in order to get all the wire out to full length. For the other three radiators, which don't go down the hill, he has hung vertically as much of the radiators as he could and then bent the remaining wire horizontally in the form of an inverted L back toward the tower riding on the rope catenaries. This system is also fed using a commercial hybrid coupler and works extremely well despite its lack of perfect symmetry. Check out Tom's 160-meter score in the 1995 *CQ* WW CW DX Contest and you will understand what I am talking about.

AUGMENT AN EXISTING TWO-ELEMENT ARRAY—ADDITIONAL LAYOUTS TO CONTEMPLATE

While the classic Four-Square system of $^1/_4$-wave radiators with $^1/_4$-wave spacing may be the most popular (and well-known) dream system in use on 160 meters today, there are a few other possibilities to augment an already existing system with two phased verticals to get more gain.

First, let's talk about expandability. It is really a "bummer" to have spent untold hours laying down a pair of vertical ground radial systems and then even *think* about having to move one or both of them. But, if you started with a $^1/_4$-wave spaced pair of inverted L antennas oriented northeast/southwest, that's exactly what you would have to do in order to expand it into a classic Four Square. You would have to push either the northeast inverted L out or push the southwest inverted L out about 60 feet in order to modify the spacing along the diagonal to the desired 190 feet.

But do you really need to do that, especially if you've already laid out 66 or 132 radials under each vertical? Could there be another way to get more gain that avoids moving either existing radiator? You bet there is—and it is actually not all that difficult to erect such a system if your property size will allow it.

A neat migration path is shown in **Fig 11-10A,** which adds a second pair of $^1/_4$-wave inverted L antennas spaced 136 feet apart ($^1/_4$ wavelength) and oriented northeast/southwest just as the original pair was, but arrayed 336 feet ($^5/_8$ wavelength) away from and parallel to the original pair. This system produces excellent unidirectional gain (about 7 dB over a single vertical radiator in fact) to either the northeast or southwest and a F/B of better than 20 dB. It is a real performer in the two principal directions most often required from much of the USA. Unlike a conventional Four-Square array, however, it doesn't allow you to switch to four directions; only two.

This layout produces a rectangular footprint on the ground, with two 136-foot long parallel sides and two 336-foot long parallel sides. The 136-foot sides run along lines facing northeast/southwest and the 336-foot sides run along lines facing northwest/southeast. It does require a few feed and design modifications compared to a two-element phased array, but these are relatively simple to implement. Here they are:

1) Each of the phasing lines must now be made an electrical $^3/_4$-wavelength long and must employ 50-Ω coax such as RG-213. Since the original pair of $^1/_4$-wave Ls used $^1/_4$-wave 50-Ω phasing lines to reach the hybrid coupler, these may be reused by adding an additional electrical $^1/_2$-wavelength of RG-213 to each. Then two new electrical $^3/_4$-wavelength phasing lines must be prepared. For purposes of clarity, we will refer to the northeast-most pair of 136-foot spaced Ls as pair A and the southwest pair of 136-foot spaced Ls as pair B.

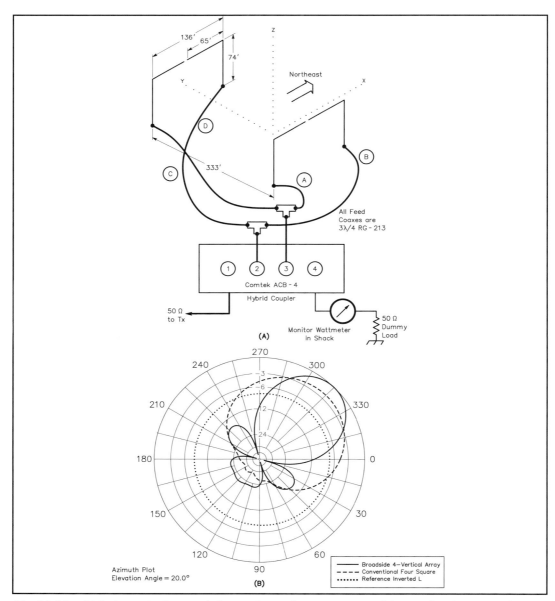

Fig 11-10—At A, layout of a much larger four-element array, with spacing between front-to-back pairs of λ/4 and side-by-side pairs of 5λ/8. This layout might result when an existing pair of radiators spaced λ/4 is augmented with another pair to get increased gain without having to relocate any radiators to create a conventional Four Square. At B, an overlay of the azimuthal responses of the broadside four-vertical array, compared with a conventional Four Square and a reference single inverted L.

2) First connect a $^3/_4$-electrical wavelength phasing line to each of the four radiators. Then place a T connector between the two phasing lines coming from pair A. Now connect a T connector between the two phasing lines coming from pair B.

3) Next we need to hook up the pairs to the hybrid coupler unit. To keep things simple, we will go for a basic system that produces two unidirectional patterns, one northeast for Europe and one southwest for VK/ZL. Assuming we are using a Comtek ACB-4 hybrid, this is done by using the 0° and 90° output ports of the hybrid. This means we put the T coming from pair A on port #2 of the hybrid and the T coming from pair B onto port #3 of the hybrid. Ports #1 and #4 are unused in this configuration.

4) Switching of the hybrid now works as follows. With the array controller inside the shack pointed to directions 1 or 2 (that is, northwest or northeast) the array fires a unidirectional pattern to the northeast. With the array controller switch pointed to directions 3 or 4 (southeast or southwest), the array fires a unidirectional pattern to the southwest. The feed line and dummy load connections into the shack remain unchanged from what was employed previously with the single pair of $^1/_4$-wave-spaced Ls northeast/southwest.

It is also possible to augment the commercial hybrid box with additional switching and phasing lines to pick up unidirectional patterns to the northwest and southeast. That is an exercise left for the experimenter handy with a grid-dip meter and a soldering gun. If anyone is genuinely interested in adding about 4 dB of uni-directional directivity to the northwest and southeast directions, please refer to the excellent article in the May/June 1996 issue of the *National Contest Journal* (*NCJ*). This was jointly authored by Peter Hutter, WW2Y, and Rob Flory, K2WI.

EXPANDING THE $^5/_8$-WAVE SPACED PAIR OF INVERTED LS

Earlier we discussed a single pair of inverted Ls oriented northwest and southeast, fed with $^3/_4$ electrical wavelength lines of RG-213 and spaced $^5/_8$ wavelength apart at 336 feet. See Fig 11-8. The system was fed as a broadside pair, in phase, to fire northeast/southwest simultaneously or, alternatively, an additional electrical $^1/_2$ wavelength line was inserted in line with either vertical to produce a bidirectional end-fire pattern firing northwest/southeast.

Assuming such a system is already in place on the ground, it can easily be expanded to a *super wide-spaced* Four-Square array by adding two more radiators, also spaced ⁵/₈-wave apart across the diagonal, in the northeast and southwest quadrants. **Fig 11-11A** shows such a system.

This system is fed with four ³/₄-wavelength phasing lines made from RG-213, one connected to each radiator. Just as in a classic Four Square, these ³/₄-wavelength phasing lines connect to an ACB-4 hybrid coupler or equivalent. Such an arrangement then yields four unidirectional patterns, each with unidirectional gain of about 5.5 dB over a single vertical radiator. The sidelobes, however, are significant compared to those in a conventional Four Square. They are down only 8 dB from peak for the larger array. See Fig 11-11B.

The principal advantage here is that you do not have to uproot a radial system in order to get your Four Square (assuming you have the necessary space); a minor disadvantage of this approach is that you blow some extra money on the two additional ³/₄-wave phasing lines and you lose a little forward gain compared to the phased end fire array just described.

Picking up radials in the woods isn't a pleasure, however, (and neither is laying them all down *again* in another location!). On the other hand, purchasing some extra coax isn't too tough, and neither is the laying out of 518 feet of RG-213 once—provided, of course, that you have the requisite amount of real estate.

THE DIAMOND FOUR SQUARE ARRAY — ANOTHER APPROACH TO EXPANDING THE NORTHWEST/SOUTHEAST ⁵/₈-WAVE-LENGTH SPACED PAIR

Assuming the existence of a ⁵/₈-wavelength spaced pair of ¹/₄-wave inverted Ls oriented northwest/southeast, the two additional radiators needed to round out the square can be added to the northeast and southwest quadrants at a relatively close spacing of 164 feet across the diagonal. The footprint for this system appears in **Fig 11-12A**, which shows the northwest/

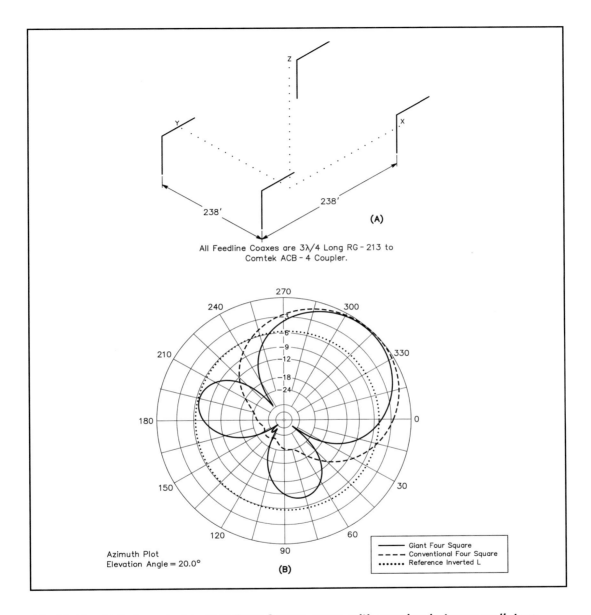

All Feedline Coaxes are 3λ/4 Long RG‑213 to
Comtek ACB‑4 Coupler.

Azimuth Plot
Elevation Angle = 20.0°

(B)

Giant Four Square
Conventional Four Square
Reference Inverted L

**Fig 11-11—At A, layout of a giant Four-Square array, with spacing between radiators
along each side of 5λ/8 (333 feet). At B, the azimuthal response of this array compared
with a conventional Four Square and a single reference inverted L. The giant array has
almost identical maximum forward gain, but it suffers from significantly degraded
sidelobes. These would degrade signal-to-noise ratio on receiving should there be
QRM/QRN or thunderstorm activities coming from those directions.**

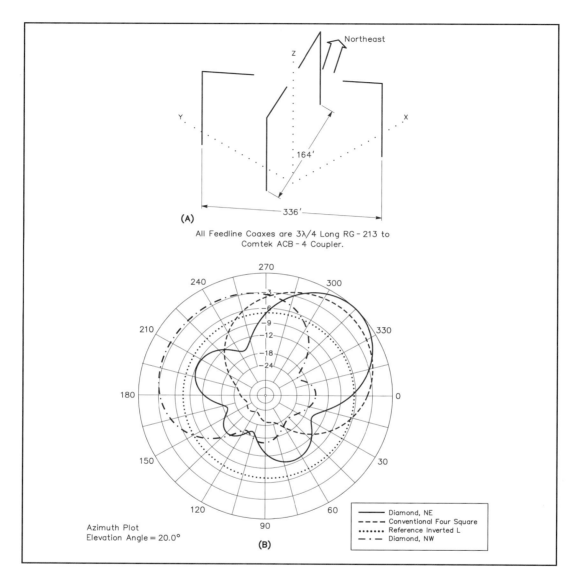

Fig 11-12—At A, layout of a diamond Four-Square array, where the spacing between the NE/SW radiators is 164 feet and the spacing between the NW/SE radiators is 336 feet. The feed system is the same used in a conventional Four Square. At B, comparison of the northeast and northwest directivity patterns, compared with the response of a conventional Four Square to the northeast and a reference single inverted L. The northwest or southeast directivity is down some 2.4 dB compared to the more favorable northeast or southwest directions. The peak gain of the larger array is about 1.2 dB more than the conventional Four Square.

southeast diagonal at 336 feet and the northeast/southwest diagonal at 164 feet.

As in the example above, this system employs $^3/_4$-electrical wavelength phasing lines made from RG-213 and is hooked up in conventional Four-Square fashion to an ACB-4 commercial hybrid or equivalent. The diamond footprint actually squeezes some extra gain from the sides of the northeast and southwest quadrants, yielding about 1.2 dB more gain than a conventional Four Square in these directions. You don't get something for nothing, however, because the gain in the northwest/southeast directions is lowered by about 1 dB compared to a regular Four Square. See Fig 11-12B.

NO ONE SIZE FITS ALL BUT THE PROOF IS IN THE PERFORMANCE

You can work a lot of DX with a single inverted-L antenna, with 16 or 32 radials under it; you might even achieve DXCC in a single season. Obviously the behemoth arrays just described are not for everyone. However, the advanced systems described here do offer relatively simple migration paths for those who may come to really love DXing and contesting on 160 meters. It is hoped that inclusion of these super arrays has provided some new ideas for some to think about.

The upper end of transmit performance on 160 meters can be achieved with these kinds of systems. Those who make the extra investment of time and effort will be richly rewarded!

Chapter 12

Simple And Effective 160-Meter Receiving Antennas

We have just reviewed some effective approaches to generating a transmit signal on Topband. Now, we must cover the receiving side of the equation with some specific and effective recommendations. After all, we don't wish to create any new 160-meter DXers who acquire reputations as *alligators* when they first venture forth to test the waters!

An alligator is a 160-meter DXer who puts out a signal that most anyone around the world can hear under good conditions. Sadly, an alligator cannot hear many of the stations responding to him because he doesn't have a proper receiving antenna. While said somewhat tongue-in-cheek, alligators on 160 meters can be a real problem when they start chasing packet spots—especially for stations they cannot hear well.

The ability to hear stations well is probably the most important and most difficult aspect of 160-meter DXing, due to atmospheric noise and the generally weak signals. Fortunately, there are some techniques to help discriminate against noise and to improve the signal-to-noise ratio of those weak DX signals entering your receiver. We will review a number of receiving antennas, starting with the classic Beverage.

THE BEVERAGE RECEIVING ANTENNA

This is probably the simplest and most effective 160-meter receiving antenna you can use on Topband. Named for its inventor, Harold Beverage, it is essentially a very long wire, aimed in the direction from which you wish to hear DX signals. A Beverage works well as a 160-meter receiving antenna because low-angle signals from the target area propagate as waves along its length and build in amplitude as they approach the antenna feed point. This also explains why the Beverage is sometimes referred to as a "traveling wave antenna."

Atmospheric noise from other directions and high-angle local signals do not propagate as well along the wire, creating a sometimes marvelous improvement in signal-to-noise ratio for low-angle signals from the desired direction. For receiving , a Beverage often "beats the pants" off most transmit antennas. In a side-by-side comparative test, very often weak signals can be heard with relative ease on a Beverage, while they cannot be copied on the transmit antenna.

Up to about 2 wavelengths at its design frequency, the longer the Beverage, the better its performance. Lengths longer than 2λ (about 1080 feet) become counterproductive, as they can create "tumbling" of the incoming waves along the wire. When this happens, cancellation occurs, which decreases the signal available at the feed point. On 160 meters, Beverages generally work well if they can be made at least 400 feet and preferably either 540 or 1080 feet in length.

The Beverage longwire can be made from any suitable insulated wire. I personally like to use #14 or #12 THHN stranded wire because it is insulated and very strong. In wooded environments, where tree branches are always falling, use of this wire for a Beverage helps keep you on the air during a storm. Insulated wire also helps to minimize rain and snow static, which can otherwise play havoc with Beverages made of bare wire. The insulation also keeps the wire from grounding out against a tree trunk or branch.

A Beverage is usually mounted 8 to 12 feet high—above human height and higher than deer or moose antlers! It is fed against ground with coax line through a suitable matching network at the feed point. The far end is terminated using a non-inductive resistor between 300 to 600 Ω. The value of this terminating resistor varies for each specific situation, depending upon soil conductivity.

A diagram of a typical Beverage antenna appears in **Fig 12-1**. A Beverage is very simple to construct—from start to finish you can install one in a few hours. You could spend even less time if supporting trees can be used as ready-made supports for the wire.

Obviously, its principal drawback is its length. You need a couple of acres of land to run even a short Beverage. Or else you need

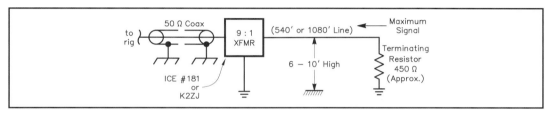

Fig 12-1—*A typical 160-meter Beverage receiving antenna. A 9:1 (50:450-Ω) transformer is used to match the 50-Ω coax line to the shack. The antenna is placed 6 to 10 feet above ground, out of the way for humans or wildlife walking under it. If the terminating resistor is omitted (allowing the end of the wire to "float"), then the Beverage becomes bidirectional. A preamplifier inside the shack or preferably at the antenna feed point (using the K2ZJ box) may improve the performance.*

some very kind neighbors who will let you run one across their land. Some 160-meter operators run their Beverages into woods adjacent to their own property, hoping they will remain undetected. Obviously, this is not a solution for everyone!

A few things need to be said about construction details but these are very straightforward. When stringing out your Beverage, standoff insulators nailed to trees or to other supports are a nice touch. It is also a good idea to use good quality 8 foot ground rods for the two ground connections and a high quality 9:1 matching transformer at the feed point. Personally, I really like the ICE Model 181 Beverage matching boxes with multiple output taps. These come equipped with an SO-239 coax input for the feed line, are fully weatherproof and include a ground screw for ground wire attachment.

If an external preamplifier is desired, the K2ZJ combination matching transformer/preamplifier unit uses the coaxial feed line to supply 12-V dc to the external preamplifier head. It is an excellent choice for feeding and matching a Beverage. ICE also manufactures a very fine Beverage termination resistor, the Model 185, but it is expensive. Connecting four 1/2-W 2200-Ω carbon resistors in parallel is a simple alternative that works just as well. However, this will not be as rugged and will not dissipate as much induced power as the ICE terminating resistor can handle. As the old saying goes: "To each his own."

Optimizing your Beverage requires some degree of care and knowledge. If you want to keep things simple, just use the 450-Ω output tap on the ICE unit at the feed point and stick a 470-Ω or 560-Ω terminating resistor between the far end of the Beverage wire and its ground stake.

If you are a purist....

My experience has shown that wet, swampy soils with good ground conductivity usually match best around 300 Ω. Sandy, lossy soils usually work best around 600 to 800 Ω. At the termination end, the process is a bit more involved and you will probably need some helpers to optimize your termination. Proper resistive termination at the far end of a Beverage to ground also varies according to soil conductivity and the height of the wire itself with respect to the ground underneath it. A value of 560 Ω is a good "ballpark" value and you may find it easiest just to go with it.

If you are a purist, however, and really want to tweak the thing, then here is how to do it. First you may want to tweak your Beverage's end termination to achieve an improvement in the front-to-back ratio. A properly terminated Beverage can have as much as 35 to 40 dB of front-to-back, giving it a true unidirectional pattern in its desired direction. To many 160-meter diehards, this is well worth the work!

You should start by inserting a small, 1000-Ω linear-taper potentiometer between your Beverage termination and its ground stake. This allows you to fine tune the resistor over the range where you are likely to find the best cancellation off the rear. To find the proper value, it is best to have another local amateur put a small amount of signal on the air on 1832 kHz at a distance of about 10 miles directly to the rear of the Beverage. This should be done during the daytime when signal levels will be most stable and the amount of RF used should be relatively low power—probably about 10 to 50 W.

The intent here is to generate about an S9 strength signal on 1832 kHz off the back of the antenna. (If this can't be done conveniently, you can achieve reasonable results using a local AM broadcast station as the signal source. However, this station must be off the back of the antenna and the signal should be in the upper end of the AM broadcast band. If possible, use an attenuator to reduce the signal level to S9 on your receiver before proceeding.)

You can monitor from inside the shack while a helper slowly turns the potentiometer. You can coordinate this part of the project using 2-meter FM handy talkies. Obviously, you want to observe the S-meter reading carefully, watching for any dip or null in that incoming S9 signal from off the back. When you find the null, remove the potentiometer and measure its value with a high quality VTVM or VOM. Then replace the pot with a fixed resistor of the same value.

Next, at the feed point end, you may want to adjust the matching transformer. If you are using the ICE unit with multiple output taps from 300 to 600 Ω, you can optimize things fairly easily. Start by attaching the feed end of the Beverage wire to the lowest output tap screw available, 300 Ω. Then put an Autek RF-1 RF Analyst on the input SO-239 of the ICE box, set the frequency to 1832 kHz and read the SWR at the feed point. Sweep the frequency across the whole 160-meter band. Write the SWR down at the low, middle and high ends of the band and then shift the Beverage wire to the next higher tap, at 450 Ω. Again read the SWR versus frequency and write it down. Now try the remaining 600-Ω tap and record the SWR across the band.

When you have checked them all, simply choose the tap with the best recorded SWR values and connect the Beverage wire to that tap. You will have now optimized the feed point transformation to the most suitable value for your Beverage and your particular soil conductivity. Maximum signal transfer can now occur from the Beverage to your feed line, which is what you are looking for. This is of major importance, of course, for weak signal 160-meter work.

If you ever wish to test the usefulness of that 9:1 matching transformer, try hooking your 50-Ω feed line directly to the end of the Beverage wire and to your ground stake. Then listen to a DX signal. You will be amazed at the difference! Matching the feed point of a Beverage is important.

The final step in this process is to record both the value of the fixed termination resistor and the output tap utilized at the feed point for future reference. You are likely to forget these over time. When a near-field lightning strike vaporizes either unit, you will be thankful that you wrote both values down—it simplifies fixing things, once the smoke clears! Take your buddies out for a beer and thank them for a job well done. Your Beverage is really ready to perform for you when it gets to be dark.

If no resistive termination to ground is employed, a Beverage will respond to low-angle signals from its rear as well as from its front. In other words, it will be bidirectional. This is sometimes even a desirable characteristic for the ham who is land-poor and has room for only one good Beverage. Aiming the front of such a Beverage at Europe from the East Coast of the USA also provides reasonable coverage into VK/ZL off the back. This can be quite useful, although those of you in the Northeast US will lose the ability to discriminate against thunderstorms coming from the US Southeast. There will be no perceptible front-to-back ratio with such a Beverage but it will usually prove to be superior compared to listening on your transmit antenna on 160 meters.

A Poor Man's Beverage

For those who are really land-poor, but have 150 to 250 feet of land available in at least some preferred direction, try replacing the Beverage with "Slinky toys" soldered together. See **Fig 12-2**. These need to be the metal variety, which are galvanized so they will accept solder. Slinkies are available from *Kay-Bee* toy outlets, from some *Toys 'R Us* outlets and from *RadioKit*, Inc, in Pelham, New Hampshire. If none of these are convenient, try calling any high-volume toy outlet in your area. After soldering a few together, suspend them from $1/4$-inch Dacron cord rope tied between two trees at opposite ends of the favored direction. The Dacron rope is passed down the center of the Slinkies first before tying it off. Then just extend the Slinkies and tie them off as well with Dacron cord so they will stay extended along the rope after installation. Make your connections just as you would with a Beverage wire at both the feed point and at the termination end. Again, if unterminated, a Slinky Beverage will also be bidirectional.

How do these things play? They are not as effective as a real, full-sized Beverage, but they do perform remarkably well. A

Fig 12-2—The "Slinky" Beverage, for those without enough land to deploy a real Beverage. The Slinky Beverage uses the popular children's toy to form a short, loaded receiving antenna.

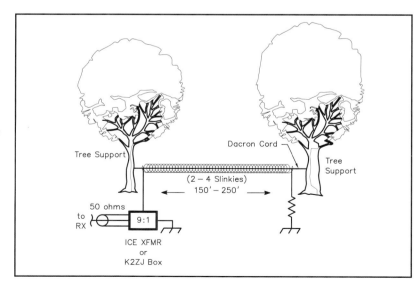

preamplifier is highly recommended, since incoming signal levels are quite low with this antenna. The preamplifier can be placed either outside at the feed point or inside the shack. Carl Huether, KM1H, who helped popularize this antenna, swears by them. I have one myself and I find it useful under some conditions, especially during periods of high summer static. It is an extremely *quiet* receiving antenna.

The Receiving "EWE" Antenna

For those on a city lot or in a subdivision wishing to improve their listening capability, the receiving "EWE" antenna may be of interest. This antenna was developed by Floyd Koontz, WA2WVL, and complete con-struction details appeared on pages 31 to 33 in February 1995 *QST*. The article was entitled "Is this EWE for YOU?" [The name is a word play on the shape of the antenna—an inverted English letter "U." The original *QST* article had a drawing of a female sheep, a "ewe" on the front page.]

A diagram of this antenna appears in **Fig 12-3**. It shows a 160/80 meter dual-band design with bottom feed. The antenna consists of a 38-foot length of horizontal wire, with 15-foot vertical sections at each end, making the total length of wire about 68 feet. Termination to ground requires an 840-Ω noninductive resistor. The basic feed impedance is conveniently about 450 Ω, meaning that an ICE Beverage matching unit with multiple outputs will work well. A 50-Ω feed line into the shack should be used and a preamplifier is desirable.

Please note from Fig 12-3 that this antenna's directivity is

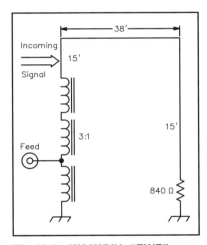

Fig 12-3—WA2WVL's "EWE" receiving antenna. The shape is that of an inverted letter "U." Because the gain is very low with this directional antenna, most builders use a receiving preamplifier to bring signals up to a useful level. Note that the 3:1 ratio in this figure is the turns ratio, meaning that the impedance step-up ratio would be 50:450 Ω. Also, the line-of-fire for the EWE is opposite that of a Beverage.

exactly opposite that of a typical Beverage. Its capture window fires away from the termination resistor rather than toward it. Remember this during construction.

I have never actually tried this antenna on 160 meters. However, it is very simple to construct and may be helpful in limited-space situations. I have received reports from people who have constructed EWEs for 80 and 160 meters. Results have been *mixed*. Some friends report terrific results with EWEs, while others have not found them to be the *magic bullets*. But, give it a try—it may work like gangbusters for EWE...

The 160-Meter Magnetic Loop Receiving Antenna

Another space-saver antenna for those with insufficient real estate available for a Beverage is the 160-meter receiving loop. A receiving loop can be constructed using 20 feet of almost any kind of coaxial line, although 50 or 75-Ω CATV Hardline seems to work best.

Construction details are shown in **Fig 12-4** so I will only review the highlights here. I like this antenna in a diamond or square configuration, 5 feet on a side. It can be tacked to the side of a tree or fastened to the crossarms of a frame made using 1.25-inch diameter wooden dowels so that it may be rotated at ground level.

The only tricky part of actual construction is to take great care making the 1-inch break in the outer shield of the coax or Hardline at the half-way point of the run of cable. The center conductor must be preserved intact when making the cut. Only the braid of the coax or the outer jacket of the Hardline is to be broken for 1 inch.

After making the cut, be sure to weatherproof this area with plenty of tape or good quality coax seal. I also like to add back some additional structural integrity to the cut point if Hardline has been used for the loop. This can be done by paralleling the break point for 6 inches on either side of the cut with $^{1}/_{2}$-inch wooden dowel before taping the weatherproof connection. This will prevent flexing of the inner center conductor of the Hardline. Too much flexing can cause metal fatigue in the center conductor.

The matching unit for this loop is a 300 to 1000 pF mica-compression capacitor (ARCO or equivalent) placed inside a small Radio Shack plastic box for weatherproofing. Three SO-239 female connectors are mounted on the box for making the

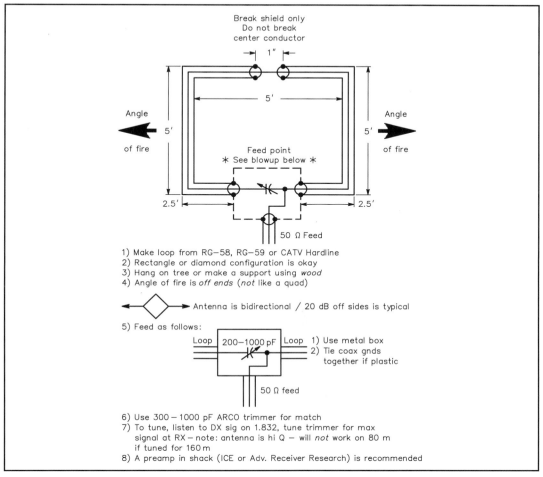

Break shield only
Do not break
center conductor

1"

5'

Angle

Angle

5'

5'

5'

5'

of fire

of fire

Feed point
* See blowup below *

2.5'

2.5'

50 Ω Feed

1) Make loop from RG—58, RG—59 or CATV Hardline
2) Rectangle or diamond configuration is okay
3) Hang on tree or make a support using *wood*
4) Angle of fire is *off ends* (*not* like a quad)

Antenna is bidirectional / 20 dB off sides is typical

5) Feed as follows:

Loop | 200—1000 pF | Loop | 1) Use metal box
2) Tie coax gnds
together if plastic

50 Ω feed

6) Use 300 — 1000 pF ARCO trimmer for match
7) To tune, listen to DX sig on 1.832, tune trimmer for max
signal at RX — note: antenna is hi Q — will *not* work on 80 m
if tuned for 160 m
8) A preamp in shack (ICE or Adv. Receiver Research) is recommended

Fig 12-4—Simple, but effective 160-meter receiving loop from K1ZM. This is made from coax or Hardline and would be hung on a tree or perhaps on a rotatable wooden frame.

loop-end and feed line connections. Remember to tie all the SO-239 shells together inside the box with solder lugs and wire if a plastic box is used.

The trimmer capacitor connects in series with the loop ends inside the box. The center conductor of the coax feed line can be attached to either side of the trimmer cap.

Tuning of the loop is very simple, since you only need to adjust the trimmer for maximum noise on 1832 kHz. When I have no helpers around, I usually accomplish this by tuning my FT-1000D to 1832 kHz and putting a small 2-meter FM H-T in front of the speaker, with the volume level turned up. After identifying, I leave the H-T in transmit mode and then quickly go outside with another H-T, listening to the incoming signal level as I turn the trimmer capacitor out at the loop.

The loop is a very high-Q circuit, causing a noticeable, sharp peak in band/signal noise when the proper value of capacitance has been found. One can "swoosh" back and forth easily to confirm the right value has been attained. If at first no peak can be discerned, try lowering the speaker volume on your receiver at 1832. It will make the peak easier to hear through the H-T. Of course, once you've finished tuning the loop, identify your call and then put the first H-T back to receive.

Once you've completed tuning the loop, replace the bottom cover of the Radio Shack box and then tape it up. I suggest that you use RG-8X or RG-58 for the feed line, since this puts a limited strain on the feed box and on the loop itself. I usually tape the coax to the 1.25-inch dowel, if used, or to the tree trunk on which the loop is mounted to finish off the project.

One important note regarding a loop's directivity—unlike a quad, which is an end-fire array through the loop's center, a receiving loop receives bidirectionally off its *ends* and not through its center. Please remember this during placement or you will be 90° off your desired capture direction!

You might wish to rotate your loop. This can be done with a Radio Shack TV rotor mounted on a TV mast 1 foot above ground level. The 1.25-inch wooden dowel mast on which the loop has been mounted is placed inside the rotator. Note that a wooden mast above the rotor is recommended—a steel mast here is not advisable. Rotation of the loop from inside the shack will produce about 20 dB of front-to-side cancellation at the 90° points as you turn the loop.

At K1ZM, I have long employed magnetic loops as receiving antennas because I know they work. They will not beat a 1080-foot long Beverage that has been properly terminated, and they do require lots of preamplification to make them "play well." In the 1995 *CQ* WW DX Contest I used a magnetic loop as my principal receiving antenna on 160 meters while operating from Cape Cod. In 30 hours of operating time, I was able to copy and log over 425 Europeans on an FT-1000D with this simple antenna! Some of the incoming signals were mere "whispers from afar" and I did need to employ almost 40 dB of preamplification to hear them, but the proof is in the pudding. Need I say more?

The LOW 160-Meter Flat-Top Dipole Receiving Antenna

Another antenna worth a try for listening on Topband is a 160-meter flat-top dipole mounted about 4 to 6 feet above ground level. Since this antenna needs to be 266 feet long, it may be necessary to position it as a rectangle around the perimeter of your property in order to fit it in. This antenna works because it is very low to the ground and this helps it to discriminate against band noise and atmospherics.

While its utility may seem somewhat suspect, I can assure you that I was very glad to have this antenna in place at my station a few years back. It was the only antenna I could copy V85AA on when Bill Maddox answered my CQ at sunrise. It certainly helped me that day. Maybe it will help you hear a rare one someday, too.

The 80-Meter Sloper as a Receiving Antenna

A number of years back I came across this one almost by accident. I hooked up by mistake my 80-meter European sloper and fed it into my 160-meter Beverage box, through my receiving preamplifier and into my receiver. Boy, was I surprised! I found that it was a terrific receiving antenna into Europe, as long as I had the preamp on. It was naturally deficient on 160 meters (since it was cut for 3650 kHz), but this seemed to help it discriminate against noise pretty well. By feeding it through my preamplifier and turning down the RF gain a bit, I found I could hear quite well with it. If you happen to have an 80-meter sloper at your QTH already, you may wish to give it a try as a 160-meter receiving antenna.

Using Your Transmit Antenna as a Receiving Antenna

If no other receiving antennas are available for DXing on 160 meters and you *must* use your transmit antenna, here are a couple of helpful suggestions. 160-meter DXing is not like normal HF DXing on 20/15/10 meters. Try backing off on your RF gain control to improve your incoming signal-to-noise ratio. Try a setting of about 2 o'clock as a starting point. If you have been listening with the RF gain wide open, you may find this an improvement. The receiver AGC will not get pumped up excessively due to static crashes. Further, the human ear can discriminate better against noise and separate the useful component of what's coming out of your headphones if it is allowed to do so at a lower level of amplitude.

For many years I would listen at sunrise using my transmit antenna. At the time, this was a folded unipole described in the previous chapter. I found I could hear some very weak Pacific stations that were way down in the noise by backing off on the RF gain control to give my ears and brain a break.

Another suggestion is to try various combinations of step attenuation, presuming that you have a receiver with this capability. If you have a preamplifier in the receiver, try switching it in and then playing with both the attenuation controls and the RF gain control in combination. It will probably take some experimenting on your part to find a combination that works best for your ears. I have also found this to be helpful when forced to listen on a transmit antenna on 160 meters.

The Multi-Position Receiver Antenna Switch

By now, it should be clear that there are a number of different receiving antennas from which to choose. You might need a *number* of different receiving antennas on 160 meters to maximize performance under varying atmospheric and band conditions. If you truly want to maximize receiver performance on Topband, then you should have as many combinations as possible in place at your station and you should be able to switch between them rapidly. For this, a good quality rotary switch is an asset and just about every top DXer I know of on 160 meters has one.

At K1ZM, I normally have about 12 to 15 receiving antennas available for instant selection! I am told that Jack, VE1ZZ, has more than 20 receiving antennas at his command. When I come upon a signal, I switch rapidly between my receiving antennas, trying to optimize for the conditions at that moment. Sometimes one of the Beverages is best. Sometimes it is one of my loops and sometimes it is the transmit Four-Square array that seems optimal at the time. Sometimes even a 45-foot piece of wire lying on the ground will outperform everything else on the rotary switch! On 160 meters, you just never know what will work best and when—so keep turning that switch.

Chapter 13

Working a DX Pileup on 160 Meters

10 TIPS FROM TODAY'S TOP DXERS

Given the weak signal levels, atmospheric noise and long, slow QSB fading unique to Topband, working a DX pileup requires a fair amount of skill and discipline in order to be successful. It is far different than on 20/15/10 meters, where signal levels are often enormous. Simply following the same approaches employed on the upper bands may be very poor practice. Without some degree of restraint and operating savvy, (read that as *common sense*), not only will *you* not work the DX station, but you could easily cause others to fail to work him.

Here are 10 suggestions that deal with proper pileup techniques on 160 meters. These are provided courtesy of Bill Tippett, W4ZV, and other fine 160-meter operators. These represent excellent advice for newcomers to the band. They will help you become a successful Topband DXer.

RULE #1

When the DX station answers someone else, *listen*; do not call. Instead, try to find where he is listening. Most good operators spread the pileup over at least 1 to 2 kHz on CW. If you listen for the station the DX is working, you will maximize your probability of being heard, since you will know where he is listening.

You may also begin to recognize the pattern the operator uses. That is, is he slowly moving up in frequency, down in frequency or alternating picks to either side of the pileup? You will also know when to transmit—when *he* is listening. It is very hard for him to hear you calling while he is transmitting!

RULE #2

Listen carefully. He may change his QSX frequency or QSY. If you are calling continuously, you will never know it. I can't tell you all the good stuff I've worked easily because I was one of the first to find a new QSX frequency. If you're transmitting continuously, you'll be one of the *last* to know. For those of you with QSK, you have an advantage here. If you don't, use a foot switch so that you can listen between calls and *stop sending* when the DX station starts.

RULE #3

Do *not* transmit on top of the station answering. Why? Because a good operator will stick with a given station until he finishes that QSO. Repeats necessitated by your QRM just reduces the amount of time *you* will have remaining to work him before propagation goes out. The name of the game is for the DX to work as many calling stations as quickly as possible. Continuously calling only slows down the whole process and reduces *your* probability of a QSO. It might also encourage some DX operators to make a mental note in their head to never "hear" you again.

There are very few DX stations and very few DXers who know how to do tail-ending effectively; that is, without causing the pileup to go out of control. My advice to DX stations and DXers on 160 meters: *Don't Try It* unless you really know what you are doing.

RULE #4

Learn your equipment so you know *exactly* how to place your transmit signal properly on frequency. No, this doesn't mean exactly zero beat on the last listening frequency, where all the other guys are. It's far better to offset by a few hundred Hz based upon which way you think the DX is tuning (see Rule #1 above). Also, *please* learn to use your equipment properly so you don't transmit on the DX frequency inadvertently. This only slows things down for everyone and wastes precious opening time on 160 meters.

RULE #5

If you have limited resources on 160 meters, focus on your *receive* antenna capability. You will work far more 160-meter DX with good ears than with a big mouth. Being an alligator who cannot hear anything is not productive on Topband.

RULE #6

Send your *full call*. Partial calls only slow things down on Topband! (Thanks, XV7SW.)

RULE #7

Use proper and consistent spacing when sending your call on CW. There are some very well known DXers who don't understand this. They will break the cadence of their calls with pregnant pauses—this can confuse a DX station trying to copy them through 160-meter QSB and QRN.

For example: W..4ZV or W4Z..V, if sent that way, can really confuse a DX station trying to copy under poor conditions. For an excellent example of how to do it right, try to emulate W3BGN's calling technique on 160. (Thanks, ZS6EZ.)

RULE #8

Send the DX station's call if you are in doubt about whom you are working. If you follow Rule #1, you will not be happy when you log a rare DX station but are actually working a different one. This is especially important if more than one DX station is listening QSX in the same general area of the band. (Thanks, 4S7RPG.)

RULE #9

Listen to the DX station's reports and match his sending speed. If he is giving out 459 reports at 18 WPM, don't reply at 35 WPM! Some claim that many high speed calls are better than low speed calls through high QRN or high QSB. I personally have never found this to be the case. But if you follow the DX station's lead, you will probably be more likely to work him by doing what *he prefers*. If the DX station is missing only your prefix or suffix, send *only* that part several times. For example: DE W4ZV, W4, W4, W4, W4ZV K or DE W4ZV, ZV, ZV, ZV, ZV, W4ZV K. It is especially important here to keep a consistent cadence (Rule #7) so that the DX can get your call correctly through the QSB and/or QRN. (Thanks, 4S7RPG.)

RULE #10

Listen...Listen...*Listen*! For those of you who still want to call continuously, I wish you luck. You'll probably be calling long after he's in my log, because I am maximizing my chances and you are minimizing yours!

73, Bill W4ZV

For those new to 160 meters who may find Bill's remarks somewhat abrasive, please be advised that there is no finer gentleman on Topband today. In addition to knowing "how to" work DX on 160 meters, Bill practices what he preaches. W4ZV, at the time this is being written, currently leads the world in countries worked on 160 meters with 290 in the log. Following his suggestions and those of the other fine DXers noted here will help you be a better and more successful 160-meter operator as you navigate the band. Happy DXing and Welcome to 160 Meters!

Chapter 14

A View of the Future

160-METER DXING CHALLENGES YET TO BE MET!

On May 1, 1981, the following exchange of views took place between Ernie Hemingway, K1PBW, and Stew Perry, W1BB:

K1PBW: "I do miss what the band was in the 1960s. I think that was the golden age of 160. I believe you'll agree. Unfortunately, few of the same fellows are on now and not many have come to take their places. It's sort of the end of an era!"

W1BB: "Yes, sort of true Ernie, I know what you mean. Yet, there are a few outstanding, pioneering type DXers still on 160, unusual DX being worked and the challenge of Topband is still there for those who want it! Although, *you* left very few challenges unmet!"

While conducting the research necessary to write this book, I chatted one evening at length with K1PBW. During that conversation Ernie asked about the state of the art on 160 meters today. He had been away from the band for over 15 years and listened intently while I described the huge Four-Square arrays in existence today. We talked about the fact that within five years, there would be the first 160-Meter DXCC issued with a 300 endorsement sticker on it. We also spoke about the kinds of almost unreal QSOs now taking place on the band via the long-path from the East Coast into XZ, 9V, 4S7, VK9X, S2 and JA.

Ernie didn't say much; he just listened. I'm not sure, but I think he was pleased that others had come to take his place as pioneers on the band and were still pushing the envelope forward, still managing to achieve first-ever QSOs that probably seemed impossible in his time—even from that fabulous 160-meter station he had assembled near Deerfield in western Massachusetts.

I have no doubt, even for a moment, that were W1BB alive today, he would be found standing along the sidelines of the playing field, waving and cheering as others continued to work new and exciting DX on 160 meters. I can almost bet Stew would want to autograph personally that first 160-Meter DXCC Award with the 300 sticker hanging proudly on it!

I have noted this historical retrospective because it is altogether fitting and appropriate that we of the *next* generation again ask ourselves at this time "What challenges yet remain on 160 meters? What is still out there yet to accomplish? Are there still any more new mountains yet to climb?" I think the answer is yes, definitely. But they are different kinds of mountains and there are, perhaps, fewer of them out there now.

OKAY, WHAT'S THE BIGGEST ONE OUT THERE...?

To me personally, the biggest task yet unmet is figuring out just what makes 160 meters *tick*? I have invested almost 20 years of my life observing this band now and I can't predict with any regularity when 1.8 MHz is going to open on the more exotic paths. And, I will bet my last dollar that no one else out there can predict the exotic openings with any degree of real accuracy either!

If this seems pretty far-fetched, here is a perfect example of what I am talking about. I noted in an earlier chapter that I checked for JA long-path from Cape Cod at 2130 Z on December 20, 21, 22, 23, and 24, 1996, with not a sign of a JA signal. Then, on December 25, I work four JAs from 2137 to 2205 Z with 579 signals. No other QSOs are made over the course of the next 9 days, although I did copy JH5FXP twice more on December 27 and 29, 1996, but with very weak signals and right at his sunrise.

What was it exactly that caused the band to open only on December 25th? Can the factors that opened the band that day be determined so that we all might know when to turn on our radios for more of the same? I surely will admit that I don't know the answer. See **Fig 14-1**, which JA3ONB prepared to show the very narrow long-path window from JA3 to K1ZM. **Fig 14-2** shows a QSL from JA4DND for December 25, 1996.

Here is another similar example. 9V1XQ and I skedded each other for four days in row early in January, 1997. No signals were heard at K1ZM during these days. Then, almost like magic, on the fifth day Mike pops in at 2242 Z, right on sked, with a solid 559 signal out of the southeast path. What set of circumstances allowed that QSO to happen? And why did I not hear any other exotic Southeastern Asians by long path over the next two weeks thereafter—even though I listened intently each and every day at my sunset?

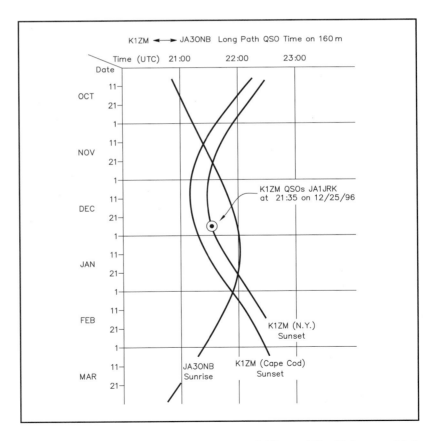

Fig 14-1—JA3ONB prepared this chart to show the very narrow long-path window from JA3 to K1ZM on 160 meters from October through March. Note that K1ZM's New York QTH window is smaller than that shown here for his Cape Cod QTH. Long-path QSOs occurred on December 25, 1996—almost the optimal date.

Fig 14-2—QSL from JA4DND, confirming QSO with K1ZM on December 25, 1996. Nice Christmas present!

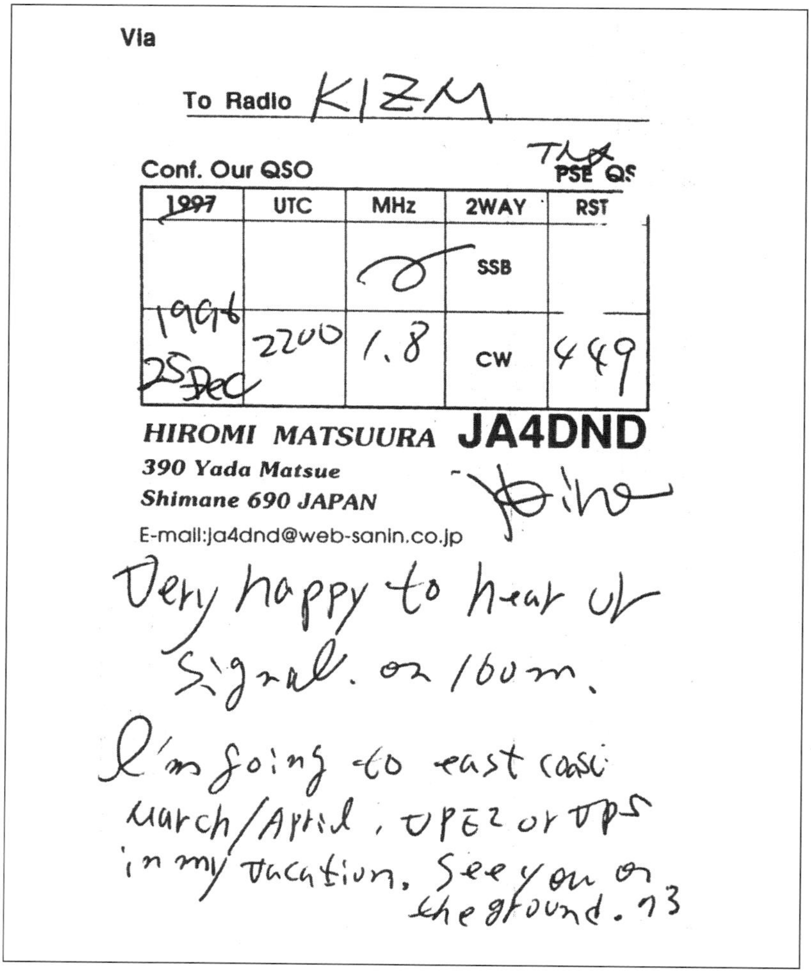

Via

To Radio K1ZM

Conf. Our QSO   THX PSE QSL

1997	UTC	MHz	2WAY	RST
		⟋	SSB	
1996 25 Dec	2200	1.8	CW	449

HIROMI MATSUURA   **JA4DND**

390 Yada Matsue
Shimane 690 JAPAN
E-mail:ja4dnd@web-sanin.co.jp

Very happy to hear ur
Signal. on 160m.

I'm going to east coast
March/April, UP E2 or UP5
in my vacation. See you on
the ground. 73

For me, the band did not open well that way again until February 4, 1997, when I worked S21XX easily at 2311 Z. But, here again, the DL boys were only a whisper over the course of the next four days while they were there. I know, I checked! February 4 was clearly a fluke and offered conditions that did not reoccur (for me at least) during the rest of their time in S2. What set of conditions came together to allow the 9V1 and the S21 QSOs to occur?

The simple and honest answer, humbling though it may be, is that we don't know! Nobody does. This is a puzzle that is still unfolding! But we do have a few *clues*. We do try to follow the WWV daily A and K indices, plus the solar flux reported from Boulder, Colorado. Topband tends to get exciting after several days of a very quiet sun, when the A and K indices have both hovered near 0 for a while.

I have long since learned, however, that this is only a partial indicator of what might happen on the band. Even when such quiet solar conditions have occurred for some days, 160 meters has not demonstrated any of the more exotic openings, even when I thought they could and should occur!

Earlier this winter season, Pierre Petry, HB9AMO, the holder of the first 40-Zone WAZ Award issued on 160 meters, noted: "I have now determined that the existence of low A and K indices are not the true drivers of propagation on 160 meters. There is something far more complex at work here!" Boy, was he ever right.

> *...many of us have observed that the first 6 hours just after a major solar flare can actually* **improve** *160-meter exotic DXing dramatically...*

What I do think can be said with some certainty is that absorption on 160 meters will be pretty awful when the A index is 30 and the K index is 6. So, the converse is true, because high A and K indices surely will make life miserable on Topband. But even here there is a subtle catch.

For a number of years now, many of us have observed that the first 6 hours just after a major solar flare can actually *improve* 160-meter exotic DXing dramatically—but only briefly! Once the ionized particles from a flare fully enter the Earth's atmosphere, it is probably a good idea to take up golf or watch a good movie for a few days. Topband is going to be pretty "punk" until things quiet down on the sun again.

We also know that the position of the auroral ovals in the Earth's polar regions seems to play a major role with respect to the ability of 160-meter signals to traverse polar paths successfully. When the auroral ovals dip down to the lower latitudes, 160-meter JA openings in the winter mornings surely seem to "go South"—literally and in a real hurry. Tom, W8JI in Georgia, still works JAs regularly while we New Englanders just sit by, barely able to hear the JAs in the upper window. So the auroral ovals are another factor controlling 160-meter propagation.

Another observation I have made in the winter is something I call "over-the-top" propagation. What I am talking about here is not some exotic opening over the Earth's polar regions. Rather, I mean the situation where the Northeast gets totally shut out of its normal dominance over the rest of the USA on the path into Europe. When over-the-top conditions occur, stations out west and down south definitely are able to hear and work western Europe at signal levels far in excess (almost 20 dB) of those of us in the northeastern US. This anomaly usually occurs during the winter months, most often in mid January into early February. I don't yet know the answer to why this occurs. While this one does seem somewhat related to high A and K indices, it's not always true.

Like many other 160-meter diehards, I long for the day when a better explanation of 160-meter propagation can be offered. I long for a better ability to *predict* propagation conditions. For now, though, I suppose the best strategy is to continue to be there, day after day, checking the possible grayline paths and hoping for an opening.

So, one of the last major mountains to climb on 160 meters is going to be the ongoing quest for an understanding of what really drives propagation on the band. This will be achieved, for me at least, when I can have a pretty clear view of when I should be investing serious listening time on 160 meters. At the moment, I contend that this is *not* known—at least not very well known.

The other challenges remaining unmet on 160 meters are probably much smaller ones, relatively speaking. Some of these include a clearer understanding of long-path propagation, both in the afternoons and in the mornings. Afternoon long-path mysteries now center on an understanding of why the path is sometimes from the northeast and sometimes from the southeast from the East Coast of the USA. Morning long-path propagation from the northeast is still a very real mystery, since so few QSOs have ever been made on this path from W1 and W2.

It is known with absolute certainty that a path exists on 7 MHz into VU at about 240° just after sunrise from W1. It is less certain that this path exists on 3.5 MHz, but it *probably* does. Who knows if it does on 1.8 MHz just before sunrise in W1? It would be great fun to have someone make a QSO someday (and live to tell about it after his or her heart starts up again)! These are the smaller mountains yet to climb for the ongoing development and understanding of 160 meters.

I should point out that many of the recent achievements "pushing the envelope on 160 meters" have probably been facilitated, at least in part, by the advent of the truly directive and relatively high-gain transmitting/receiving arrays now in existence. The growing popularity of the superlative Four-Square array on 160 meters is just now beginning to unlock some of the last "doors" on the band by making such exotic QSOs somewhat commonplace. It certainly hasn't been a major breakthrough in receiver technology that has allowed these QSOs to occur. Transmitter power levels have been at or near a kW for quite some time now in most parts of the developed world.

As we move into the next sunspot minimum, I suspect a few more doors will be opened with respect to understanding the true drivers of 1.8-MHz propagation. I also suspect, though, that Stew Perry's comment to K1PBW that "the challenge of Topband is still there for those who want it" will still be just as valid as it is today.

That challenge has kept me an interested Topband student for quite a long time now. I love the challenges of 160 meters. I suspect most other serious 160-meter DXers do as well. It still remains the last band where you cannot buy success with your plastic charge card. Neither will you ever really know what is going to come out of your radio when you sit down at sunset or sunrise! Maybe it is best that the full story of propagation on 160 meters never be wholly understood. After all, it might make the band "boring"—for N6TR (who lives in Boring, Oregon) and all the rest of us!

Chapter 15

A Photographic Potpourri

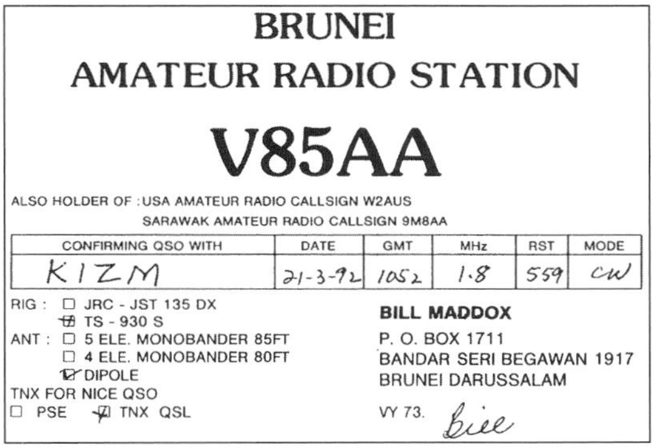

BRUNEI
AMATEUR RADIO STATION
V85AA

ALSO HOLDER OF : USA AMATEUR RADIO CALLSIGN W2AUS
SARAWAK AMATEUR RADIO CALLSIGN 9M8AA

CONFIRMING QSO WITH	DATE	GMT	MHz	RST	MODE
K1ZM	21-3-92	1052	1.8	559	CW

RIG : ☐ JRC - JST 135 DX
     ☑ TS - 930 S
ANT : ☐ 5 ELE. MONOBANDER 85FT
     ☐ 4 ELE. MONOBANDER 80FT
     ☑ DIPOLE
TNX FOR NICE QSO
☐ PSE ☑ TNX QSL

BILL MADDOX
P. O. BOX 1711
BANDAR SERI BEGAWAN 1917
BRUNEI DARUSSALAM

VY 73. *Bill*

Fig 15-1—QSL for 160-meter QSO between
K1ZM and V85AA in Brunei. A low 160-
meter dipole was the receiving antenna at
K1ZM to copy Bill at sunrise on the East
Coast.

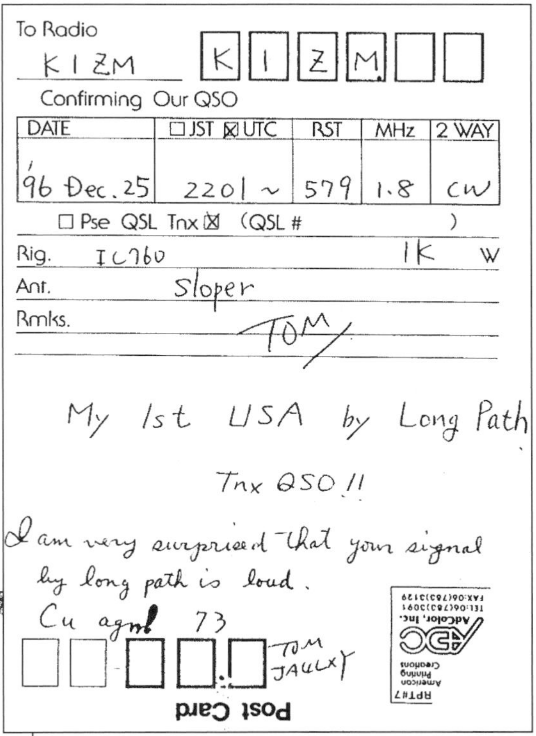

To Radio
K1ZM   K | 1 | Z | M
Confirming Our QSO

DATE	☐ JST ☒ UTC	RST	MHz	2 WAY
96 Dec. 25	2201 ~	579	1.8	CW

☐ Pse QSL Tnx ☒ (QSL #   )

Rig. IC760   1K W
Ant.   Sloper
Rmks.   TOM.

My 1st USA by Long Path

Tnx QSO !!

I am very surprised that your signal
by long path is loud.
Cu agn! 73
            TOM
            JA4LXY

Post Card

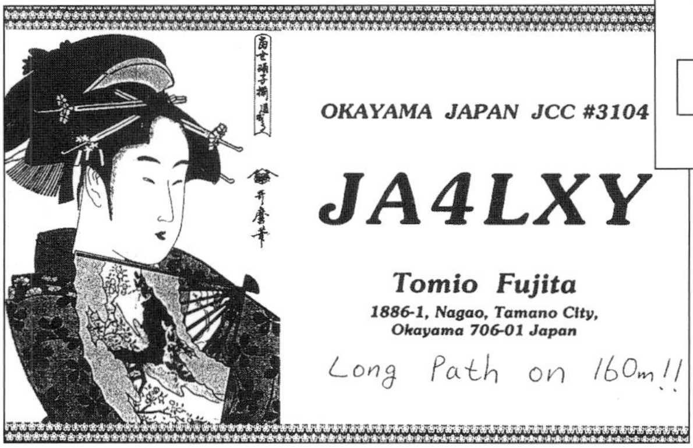

RPT47
American
Printing
Creations
ADColor, Inc.
TEL:06(763)3091
FAX:06(763)3129

OKAYAMA JAPAN JCC #3104

JA4LXY

Tomio Fujita
1886-1, Nagao, Tamano City,
Okayama 706-01 Japan

Long Path on 160m !!

Fig 15-2—QSL confirming 160-meter
long-path QSO between K1ZM and
JA4LXY on December 25, 1996.

9V1 XQ

MICHAEL SELBY
WA2DWE
YB0ARS
P29SR

6 CORONATION RD. W.
BLOCK 329 #0401 RIVER VALLEY RD.
SINGAPORE 0923 1026

CALL K1ZM
DATE 11·1·97   TIME 2242 Z
FREQ. 1.825 CW SIGNAL 569

All the best Jeff, glad
to make contact.

73
Mike

Fig 15-3—QSL from 9V1XQ, confirming long-path QSO with K1ZM on January 11, 1997.

Fig 15-4—Two of UK's finest, Clive, GM3POI (left), and Dave, G4BUO (right).

Fig 15-5—Gary, KD9SV, one of the better 160-meter signals out of the US Midwest.

Fig 15-6—The "Green Hornet" himself: Bob, W3GH. Bob is one of a handful of North American stations who have worked Mount Athos on 160 meters.

Fig 15-7—Roger, G3SXW, of ZD9SXW fame. Only a handful of 160-meter DXers managed to snare Roger at ZD9. Well done, everyone!

Fig 15-8—Paul, 5X4F (right) with Lamar, W9LT. Paul has provided many 160-meter DXers with the rare 5X and 5Z QSOs.

Fig 15-9—George, K8GG (center), one-third of the "Battle Creek Special" crew, with XYL at left and Dave, KJ9I (right).

Fig 15-10—Richard, K5NA and XYL Susan, KU2Q, back in Texas again, chasing 160-meter DX and contesting.

Fig 15-11—Gary, NI6T, one of the big guns on the US "left coast" these days.

Fig 15-12—Ike, K8IP, always in there with a FB Topband signal.

Fig 15-13—Rio, JA1JRK, holding QSL from K1ZM for their long-path QSO on December 25, 1996. Rio's 80 and 160-meter signals are outstanding.

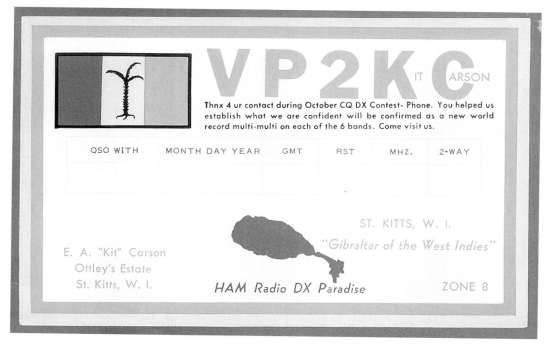

Fig 15-14—VP2KC QSL card from 1979 CQ WW multi-multi effort.

Fig 15-15—The VP2KC 80-meter phased array (beyond the two towers), viewed from the air. K1PBW said: "I worked my butt off putting all this stuff up."

Fig 15-16—A group of prominent 160-meter operators, at Oxford 1986. Left to right: Nev, G3RFS; Willem, PAØHIP; Dave, G3SZA; Roger, G3RBP and Clive, G3ZFC. Picture taken by G3PQA.

Fig 15-17—Some 160-meter DL enthusiasts. There's many a 160-Meter DXCC certificate held among this fine group of operators. Left to right: Hans, DL8NBE; Hans, DL6WV; Gun, DL1BU; Peter, DJ8WL; Jan, DL9KR; Walt, DJ6QT and Jo, DL1RK.

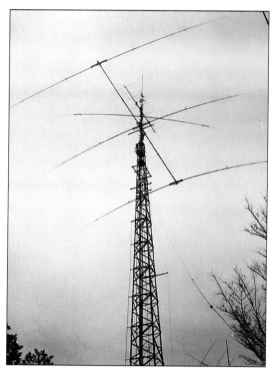

Fig 15-19—Now you know why JA1JRK is loud on the low bands. Rio suspends a 160-meter delta loop from the top of the 150-foot tower that also supports the three-element 80-meter Yagi.

Fig 15-18—Kuny, JA7NI, celebrating another 160-meter "new one." His 130-foot towers support the vertically polarized 160-meter delta loop. Kuny has had one of the best 160-meter signals from Japan for 20 years.

Fig 15-20—Hiro, JA4DND, in his shack. K1ZM confirmed their long-path QSO with an eyeball QSO at K1ZM in March 1997.

Fig 15-21—Tom, JA4LXY, in his shack. He is 41 years old and has worked 189 countries on Topband from JA. Outstanding job, Tom!

Fig 15-23—Tom, JA7OEM, sure pokes a fine Topband signal out of Yamagata with this neat setup. The antenna at JA7OEM is a pair of halfwave slopers from a 120-foot tower.

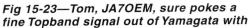

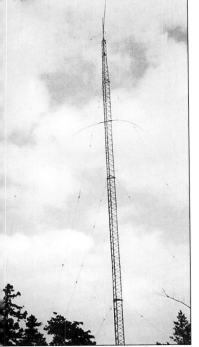

Fig 15-22—The antenna farm at JA4LXY. Tom uses a 160-meter sloper for his transmit antenna, suspended from a 72-foot tower.

(A)

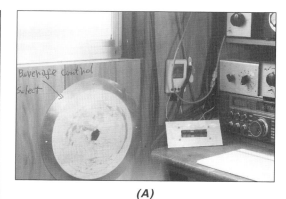

(A)

(B)

Fig 15-24—At A, Ken, JA0MVW, in his
shack. Ken listens on the small receiving
loop shown at B. We know it works,
judging from the number of East Coast
USA stations he has worked on Topband.

(B)

Fig 15-25—The shack of Saka, JA1HQT. At
A, his Beverage selection and display
system, using a world map and a 12-
position switch. The Beverages range in
length 360 to 790 feet. At B, close-up of
the matching box for one of his
Beverages.

Fig 15-26—Jose, EA3VY (left), and Dave, G3SZA, at Dayton, 1984. Photo by Joe, LU2DX.

Fig 15-27—Rick, K5UR (at left, with XYL Holly), and Bob, W3GH, and Paul, N4PN, at Dayton. Holly is renowned as a tower climber.

Fig 15-28—Bob, VS5RP, in 1980. This preceded his 160-meter postings to P29PR and 4S7RPG.

Fig 15-29—The shack at EA8AK.

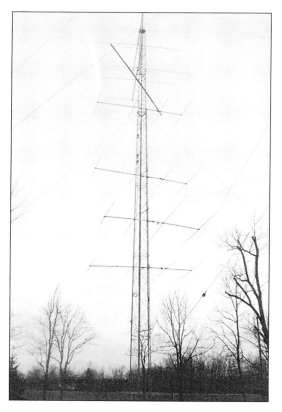

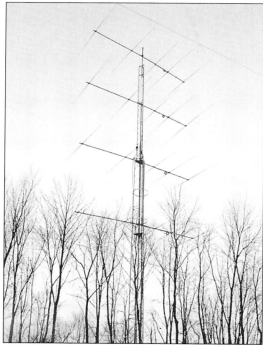

Fig 15-30—Some of the antennas at K9UWA. Wow!

Fig 15-31—Ruda, OK1DTN, and Petr, OK1DOT, taken in 1986.

Fig 15-32—Hal, W2TQC, at Dayton.

Fig 15-33—Sunset over the 160-meter Four Square array at AA0RS.

Fig 15-34—Dave, AA0RS (G3SZA) at his Colorado QTH in 1996.

Fig 15-35—Woody, K2UU (left), at Dayton, with a friend.

Fig 15-36—From left to right: K1VR, VE3BMV, G3SZA, W8LRL and NP4A at Dayton.

Fig 15-37—Gerry, W1ZM (left), and Jeff, K1ZM, next to W1ZM's 160-meter vertical.

Fig 15-38—Paul, WØAIH, and XYL Mary, in 1983.

Fig 15-39—John, W2JB (left); Dave, G3SZA (center), and Tony, K2SG (right) at Dayton.

Fig 15-40—The shack of Clarry, VK5KL, one of the better VK signals on Topband over the years.

Fig 15-42—Arch Doty, K8CFU.

Fig 15-41—Jorge, LU7XP, in his shack in 1980. His signal was for many years one of the best from LU.

Fig 15-43—Don, N4IN, about 1985. Don was the contest manager of the CQ 160-Meter Contest and an active 160-meter DXer too.

Fig 15-44—Jim, W2PV, and XYL Molly about 1980, standing next to rotating "Big Bertha" array.

Fig 15-45—Jeff, K1ZM (left) with Wal, W8LRL (right), standing next to Wal's 160-meter vertical in 1988.

Fig 15-46—1985 RSGB Convention. From left to right: G4AAW, 4X4NJ, G3ZFC, G4AKY, G3NKC, G3XTT, G4FPH, G3AIK, PAØHIP, G3RTY, G3SZA, G3YMC, G3SFT, G3KMA, GM3YOR, G6CJ, G3RBP, G3RFS, G3RAU, G3RPB, G3CWI, G3PQA.

Fig 15-47—Bob, 9M4LP (EP2BK) and the local G-land 160-meter crowd, in 1966. At rear, left to right: 9M4LP, G3TLY, G3RAU, G3TZM and G3SED. At front, left to right: G3SZA and G3RFS.

Fig 15-48—John, W3ESU (left); Laci, W1PL (center), and Dave, N4SU (right). Fine 160-meter operators all!

Fig 15-49—Dom, I8UDB (left), with Jeff, K1ZM (right). I8UDB puts out a great signal out of Naples on 80 and 160 meters!

Fig 15-50—A group of prominent JA DXers. From left to right: Ogi, JA1CGM; Toshi, JA1ELY; Key, JR1EBE; Yuki, JA6LCJ and Hiro, JF1NZW at top in Tokyo, 1991.

Fig 15-51—Jim, K9JF/7 at K1ZM, October 1995.

Fig 15-52—Steve Sussman, W3BGN, in his Pennsylvania shack. Steve has confirmed 272 DXCC countries on 160 meters, leading the Frankford Radio Club, and among the top total worldwide! FB, Steve. He uses a full-wave loop as a transmitting antenna.

Fig 15-53—At the JF1NZW QTH, mid 1980s. From left to right: JF1NZW; Ross, 9M2AX; JA1GTF; JA1CHN.

Fig 15-54—Rudy, DK7PE, at Dayton 1996. This fine DXer always puts out a great 160-meter signal wherever he goes!

Fig 15-55—A 1987 Who's Who in OK land. At top, left to right: OK3CSQ, OK4DXS, OK1DRU, OK1DOT, OK1DTN, OK1FDY. At bottom, left to right: OK3TRJ, OK1DQT, OK3CQD, OK1JDX, OK1DWJ, OK3CQR, OK3CWQ. (Thanks, OK1DOT.)

Fig 15-56—Take, JA5AUC (left), with Hiro, JA4DND, at K1ZM in March 1997.

UZBEKSTAN REPUBLIC

UK8LA

CONFIRMING QSO WITH   *K1ZM*

DATE			GMT	MHz	MODE	RST
D	M	Y				
18·02·96			23.23	1.824	CW	549

73 *KARIM*

PSE QSL TNX

A.R.S. UK8LA.
P.O.BOX 13
BOUKHARA 705000
UZBEKISTAN

Fig 15-57—QSL card from UK8LA to K1ZM, confirming QSO of February 18, 1996.

Colombo, Sri Lanka

4S7RPG

To....*K1ZM*....confirming our..*CW*..QSO on..*8 FEB 97*..

at....*0104*...hrs UTC on....*1·8*....MHz Ur RST..*449*..

Rig....*TS-430*....power..*100*..watts Antenna..*Inv -L*..
18 metres

Pse/Tnx QSL via Bureau/Direct

P.O. Box 987,
Colombo, Sri Lanka

73s......R.E. Parkes
G3REP EX-VS5RP, P29PR, A45XF

Fig 15-58—QSL from 4S7RPG to K1ZM for long-path QSO on February 8, 1997. Wow!

Notes

Notes

Notes

Notes

FEEDBACK

Please use this form to give us your comments on this book and what you'd like to see in future editions, or e-mail us at **pubsfdbk@arrl.org** (publications feedback). If you use e-mail, please include your name, call, e-mail address and the book title, edition and printing in the body of your message. Also indicate whether or not you are an ARRL member.

Where did you purchase this book?
☐ From ARRL directly   ☐ From an ARRL dealer

Is there a dealer who carries ARRL publications within:
☐ 5 miles   ☐ 15 miles   ☐ 30 miles of your location?   ☐ Not sure

License class:
☐ Novice   ☐ Technician   ☐ Technician Plus   ☐ General   ☐ Advanced   ☐ Amateur Extra

Name _____

Daytime Phone (   )_____

Address _____

City, State/Province, ZIP/Postal Code _____

If licensed, how long?_____

Other hobbies _____

_____

Occupation _____

ARRL member? ☐ Yes ☐ No
Call Sign _____
Age _____
e-mail _____

For ARRL use only	DXING ON EDGE
Edition	1 2 3 4 5 6 7 8 9 10 11 12
Printing	2 3 4 5 6 7 8 9 10 11 12

From _____

_____

_____

EDITOR, DXING ON THE EDGE
AMERICAN RADIO RELAY LEAGUE
225 MAIN STREET
NEWINGTON CT 06111-1494

— — — — — — — — — — please fold and tape — — — — — — — — — — — —

DXING ON THE EDGE—
THE THRILL OF
160 METERS

PROOF OF
PURCHASE

Memorable Moments on 160 Meters

NOTES FOR THE AUDIO CD

By Jeff Briggs, K1ZM

Track 1: Foreword by K1ZM
W1BB himself, with K1PBW, EI8H, W9UCW and W9HT (December 31, 1977)

Track 2: Interview with Ralph Green, W1HT (ex W1HGT)

Track 3: Some familiar call signs, recorded in Europe at DJ8WL
W8LRL, KV4FZ, W1BB/1, K1PBW

Track 4: Stew Perry working UK2PCR, country #150, recorded at DJ8WL

Track 5: KL7Y works DJ8WL

Track 6: Far East signals, heard in Europe at DJ8WL
JA6LCJ, VS6DO, JA2GQO, KP4KK/DU2

Track 7: Other well-known DXers, heard at DJ8WL
AA1K, W4PZV, PY1RO, NP4A (1982), K1ZM (1984), W9ZR, N5JJ, N4IN, WA2SPL, G3SZA, 4X4NJ, XRØY (September 1995), CEØZ (September 1995)

Track 8: First JA to Caribbean, at NP4A
JA2GQO, following first JA/Caribbean QSO in January 1981

Track 9: Japan to USA East Coast, recorded at K1ZM
JA1HQT (January 23, 1997)

Track 10: Hong Kong to K1ZM
VS6DO (December 22, 1988)

Track 11: Some famous DXers, as heard at K1ZM
KH6CC (1985), W5FXP, K1ZM, F8VJ (1985), 4X4NJ (1984), D44BC (1984), HB9AMO (1984), UG6GAW (1984), DJ8WL (1984), DK8NG (1985), ZL2BT (1984), PY1RO (1984), CP8HD (1984), PY1BVY (1984), WA3EUL (1984), HC1BI (1984), JE1SPY (1985), JF1NZW (1985), HZ1AB (1984)

Track 12: Bob Parkes, A45XF, recorded at G3PQA (1993)

Track 13: Searchlight propagation: K2EK at ZL3GQ (January 1986)

Track 14: Other signals recorded at ZL3GQ (January 1986)
K5NA, AA1K, W1CF, WØZV, N6DX, VO1HP, KP2J

Track 15: A really exotic QSO for K1ZM, recorded by VE1ZZ (November 21, 1996)
XZ1N

Track 16: Final comments by K1ZM